Man in Nature

SECOND EDITION

FOUNDATIONS OF MODERN BIOLOGY SERIES

MAN IN NATURE, SECOND EDITION, *Marston Bates*

FOUNDATIONS OF MODERN BIOLOGY SERIES

William D. McElroy and Carl P. Swanson, Editors

Design by Walter Behnke

Current printing (last digit):
12   11   10   9   8   7   6

PRENTICE-HALL INTERNATIONAL, INC., *London*

PRENTICE-HALL OF AUSTRALIA, PTY., LTD., *Sydney*

PRENTICE-HALL OF CANADA, LTD., *Toronto*

PRENTICE-HALL OF INDIA PVT. LTD., *New Delhi*

PRENTICE-HALL OF JAPAN, INC., *Tokyo*

C-55191(p)   *C-55192(c)*

Donald Gray

PRENTICE-HALL FOUNDATIONS OF MODERN BIOLOGY SERIES

William D. McElroy and Carl P. Swanson, Editors

NEW VOLUME

Chemical Background for the Biological Sciences, Emil H. White

SECOND EDITIONS

The Cell, Carl P. Swanson

Cell Physiology and Biochemistry, William D. McElroy

Heredity, David M. Bonner and Stanley E. Mills

Adaptation, Bruce Wallace and Adrian M. Srb

Growth and Development, Maurice Sussman

Animal Physiology, Knut Schmidt-Nielsen

Animal Diversity, Earl D. Hanson

Animal Behavior, V. G. Dethier and Eliot Stellar

The Life of the Green Plant, Arthur W. Galston

The Plant Kingdom, Harold C. Bold

Man in Nature, Marston Bates

MARSTON BATES   *University of Michigan*

Englewood Cliffs, N. J.   **PRENTICE-HALL, INC.**

To **Henry Allen Moe** who as Secretary General of the Guggen-heim Foundation has generously supported studies both of man and of nature, and, more importantly, has fostered that creative spirit which in the long run is the best excuse for being human.

Foundations
of Modern Biology
Series

The science of biology today is *not* the same science of fifty, twenty-five, or even ten years ago. Today's accelerated pace of research, aided by new instruments, techniques, and points of view, imparts to biology a rapidly changing character as discoveries pile one on top of the other. All of us are aware, however, that each new and important discovery is not just a mere addition to our knowledge; it also throws our established beliefs into question, and forces us constantly to reappraise and often to reshape the foundations upon which biology rests. An adequate presentation of the dynamic state of modern biology is, therefore, a formidable task and a challenge worthy of our best teachers.

The authors of this series believe that a new approach to the organization of the subject matter of biology is urgently needed to meet this challenge, an approach that introduces the student to biology as a growing, active science, and that also *permits each teacher of biology to determine the level and structure of his own course*. A single textbook cannot provide such flexibility, and it is the authors' strong conviction that these student needs and teacher prerogatives can best be met by a series of short, inexpensive, well-written, and well-illustrated books so planned as to encompass those areas of study central to an understanding of the content, state, and direction of modern biology. The FOUNDATIONS OF MODERN BIOLOGY SERIES represents the translation of these ideas into print, with each volume being complete in itself yet at the same time serving as an integral part of the series as a whole.

PREFACE TO THE SECOND EDITION

The first edition of the FOUNDATIONS OF MODERN BIOLOGY SERIES represented a marked departure from the traditions of textbook writing. The enthusiastic acceptance of the Series by teachers of biology, here and abroad, has been most heartening, and confirms our belief that there was a long-felt need for flexible teaching units based on current views and concepts. The second edition of all volumes in the Series retains the earlier flexibility, eliminates certain unnecessary overlaps of content, introduces new and relevant information, and provides more meaningful illustrative material.

The Series has also been strengthened by the inclusion of a new volume, *Chemical Background for the Biological Sciences* by Dr. Emil White. The dependence of modern biology on a sound foundation in physics and chemistry is obvious; this volume is designed to provide the necessary background in these areas.

In preparing the second edition of the Series, the authors and editors gratefully acknowledge the many constructive criticisms that have been made by hundreds of teaching biologists. Their interest and aid have made the task of writing more a pleasure than a burden.

Contents

ix

MAN IN NATURE

The Human
Animal

CHAPTER ONE

Man is clearly an animal. If you cut a specimen open, you find that the parts—heart, intestines, liver, lungs—differ little from the corresponding organs of dogs, cats, or monkeys. If you study his respiration, digestion, reproduction, muscle contraction, nerve or endocrine coordination, you find the same general processes and the same general chemical and physical relations that you find in other animals. If you are interested in classification, you have no difficulty in recognizing that man is a vertebrate and hence belongs to the phylum Chordata. Among the vertebrates, he obviously belongs with the class of mammals. Although he has an unusually small amount of hair, other mammals have even less—whales, for instance. He is bipedal, using only his hind legs for locomotion, but this is true also of kangaroos. Men, monkeys, and apes are very similar in the details of their anatomy, and among the mammals it is customary to group them together as an order, the primates.

Yet, equally unquestionably, man is very peculiar, so different from everything else that you can plausibly argue that he is not really an animal at all but a quite new sort of phenomenon in the world. This difference, when analyzed, turns not on anatomy and physiology, but on behavior and accomplishment. The difference is clear, but its cause or basis, the way in which it developed, and its essential nature, are not easily described or analyzed.

The human difference is most easily labeled with the anthropological word "culture." By culture is meant the way of life, the accumulated tradition, knowledge, and customs of a people, transmitted from generation to generation and from individual to individual by teaching and learning. Every man has two inheritances: the biological, genetic inheritance of his animal nature, and the cultural inheritance which depends largely on language, on symbol systems.

Human behavior is so complex that it has become the subject of several distinct sciences, which are grouped together as the "social sciences." In general we can distinguish among the physicochemical, biological, and social sciences. The physicochemical sciences are concerned with the inanimate forces and materials of the universe; the biological sciences with the special properties of life; the social sciences with the special properties of culture. Perhaps some day the social and cultural behavior of man will be explicable in biological terms—and ultimately again in physicochemical terms. But we are a long way from any such eventuality now, and these various groups of sciences must each use rather different methods and delve into different kinds of problems.

A real unity does exist in science, however; there is a continuity between physical and biological sciences, on the one hand, and biological and social sciences on the other. Biochemistry and biophysics provide convenient labels for the one continuity; the other, no less important, is not so obviously labeled. The aim of this book is to explore the area of contact and overlap between the biological and social sciences, to look at some of the parts of biology that provide useful background for the exploration of social studies.

THE SCIENCES CONCERNED WITH MAN

Psychology and anthropology are the social sciences most clearly related to biology. Both, in fact, include large areas of knowledge that could be regarded as purely biological. Comparative psychology deals with the behavior of animals—or may even be extended to include plant behavior. Experimental psychology always includes much biological material, even when the experiments involve human subjects and are aimed at solving human problems. Physical anthropology is also largely a biological science, and covers genetics, human physical types, and racial diversity, and fossils of men or man-like animals. Physical anthropology, therefore, is that part of the science concerned with man as an animal; the other parts of anthropology concentrate more on man as a bearer of culture.

The distinctions among social psychology, social anthropology, and sociology are far from clear-cut. Differences in points of view, methods, and problems dealt with are most easily explained in terms of the historical development of the different sciences. Psychology, traditionally, has been concerned with the behavior of men as individuals. Anthropology started as the study of exotic people, strange tribes with strange ways, and, through its branch of archaeology, also encompassed the prehistoric past. Sociology, in its beginnings, investigated the institutions of Western civilization, things like class structure, urbanization, religious and educational institutions. These distinctions have long been blurred, but they are still discernible.

Since sociology has been mainly focused on the institutions of civilization, it has had less direct contact with biology than its sister sciences. Yet a prime interest of sociology is the study of human populations, which forms the subject of the special science of *demography*. The study of human populations and the study of the populations of other organisms have much in common, and the two subjects have become closely related. It is interesting that the vocabulary and concepts used in population study were for the most part first developed by demographers, and subsequently applied to organisms other than man.

Sociology has also directed its attention to the environmental relations of men and human institutions, and has developed a special field called human ecology. The relations between human and other kinds of ecology, however, have not been carefully worked out, and there is considerable disagreement about the meaning of the term. Human ecology, however defined, is close to human geography, which is generally considered to be another social science. Economics, curiously, has the same Greek root as ecology (*oikos,* meaning household), and phrases like "the economy of nature" and "the ecology of man" illustrate how easily the two words may be interchanged. But as the sciences are practiced in our universities, there is little connection between ecology and economics.

BIOLOGICAL AND SOCIAL SCIENCES

The relationship between the biological and social sciences begins with the problem of the biological roots of cultural phenomena. We are here concerned with the differences between man-as-an-animal and man-as-a-bearer-of-culture. One extreme view holds that human behavior is culturally determined and that man's animal background is irrelevant and meaningless. The other extreme considers that since man so obviously is an animal, everything about him must have a biological explanation.

The truth probably lies somewhere in between. Man has retained his animal constitution which forms, however distantly, a background for his actions; but his actions are more than those of just an animal. Nutrition and reproduction, for instance, are universal biological drives found in all organisms. Yet food behavior and sexual behavior in man cannot be understood in purely biological terms. What one eats, when one eats, how one eats, whom one eats with vary greatly from culture to culture and are clearly learned patterns of behavior. Hunger, however, still has a physiological basis; digestion is still a chemical process, even though this does not explain why, among some peoples, ants are highly prized food while, among others, the idea of eating ants is horrifying. The hunger drive may be thwarted by fasting, for cultural reasons, and sometimes men will die rather than eat food they believe unfit.

Sex similarly is channeled by custom and by culture among all known peoples. There are always rules about who may marry whom, and there is always a taboo against incest—though what is considered to be incest may vary tremendously. Man is extraordinary among animals in having a continuous sexuality; he is also extraordinary in suppressing that sexuality in cults of chastity. The immense variety of forms of individual or institutional sexual behavior of different peoples can hardly be explained biologically, but underneath there is a biological drive which is related to the biological drive in all forms of sexual reproduction. But how, with all of this complexity, do we find the biological basis? How do we determine what is innate, instinctive, "natural" for man?

The concept of evolution teaches us that the cultural grew out of the biological just as, at another level, the living grew out of the inorganic. Life started, somehow, as a development from inorganic processes; and culture started, somehow, from biological origins. But once culture started, once man started transmitting learned behavior from generation to generation, human behavior began to take on special aspects.

Every man is the consequence of his two inheritances. We can call one somatic and the other extrasomatic. The somatic inheritance is biological, and depends on genes and chromosomes; the extrasomatic is cultural, and depends on symbolic forms of communication. We can find all sorts of analogies between the two systems. The symbol systems on which tradition depends compare with the genetic systems on which biological inheritance depends. Cultural traits are adaptive, in many ways, as are biological traits, and the various kinds of adaptations can be studied. The diffusion of cultural traits can be traced and we see blending or hybridization—and conflict —in cultures. But it is dangerous to forget that we are dealing with two very different systems. That the two often show analogies does not mean that they are the same thing. We can learn much about each of the systems, however, by studying the analogies—if we are careful—and it is unfortunate that the two systems are generally studied by quite different people, working in different scientific worlds.

If we look at the man-and-culture relationship from the point of view of organism and environment, we are confronted with this question: Is culture an attribute of the human organism, or is it part of the human environment? The ways of answering this can serve as a somewhat oversimplified distinction between the psychological and anthropological views of man. Psychologists tend to consider culture as a part of the environment: they concentrate on the reactions of the individual to his culture, how he copes with it or fails, how he becomes adjusted or frustrated. The anthropologist, on the other hand, tends to regard culture as a part of the man: When he studies Dyaks in Borneo or Hopi in the United States and describes their ways of life, he is analyzing the adjustments of man and culture to the environment.

For the biologist, culture must at times be viewed as part of the man, at other times as part of the environment. We must always be aware that we are dealing with the man-culture-environment complex. When we study man's ecological relationships, it is generally man and culture versus the environment that interests us. The ecological character of a man in the Congo, for instance, depends on whether he is a food-gathering pygmy, an agricultural Bantu, or an industrialized Belgian.

On the other hand, when we study man's physiology, it is more useful to treat culture as a part of the environment. If we are interested in the heat relations of the human animal, for example, his clothing and housing and his work habits become environmental effects. Cultural influences are so pervasive that the study of human biology, or man's uncultured physiology, is made very difficult. Temperature relations, nutritional needs, sexual behavior, excretory functions, all the basic physiological processes, may be influenced in many subtle ways by cultural factors. This fact sometimes disrupts cross-cultural medical work. Treatment effective in the United States of Europe may not necessarily be equally applicable in China or tropical Africa. The effect of chemicals on pathogens remains the same, but the human factor, the human reaction, may vary greatly.

But what are the peculiar characteristics of man? What do all men share that other animals do not have? We might try to sort out these qualities, lumping what may be trivial with what may be important, under the headings of physical, behavioral, and cultural characteristics.

Physical Characteristics

Man's most striking anatomical characteristics stem from his upright posture and bipedal locomotion. The habit of walking on the hind legs, which leaves the hands and arms—the forelegs—free at all times for manipulating or carrying objects, involves numerous anatomical changes. Man's legs, unlike those of the great apes and most other primates, are much longer than the arms (Figs. 1-1, 1-2), and there are many alterations in the pelvic region, especially the ilium. Man's foot, with the great toe in line with the other toes and with the high arch, is quite different from the foot of apes; it is well adapted to walking or running, but not much good for grasping branches. The head is poised on the spinal column so that man looks forward when standing upright.

Man has a very large brain compared with those of apes and other

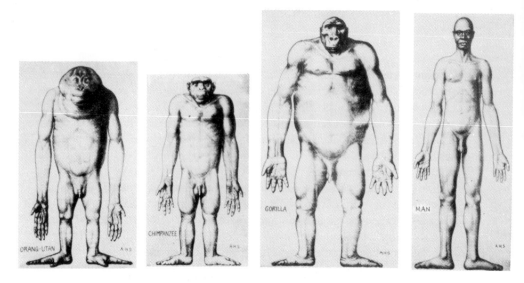

Fig. 1-1. Comparative proportions of great apes and man. (Reprinted from Adolph H. Schultz, "The Skeleton of the Trunk and Limbs of Higher Primates," Human Biol., **Vol. 2, No. 3, Sept., 1930. By permission of the Wayne State Univ. Press.** © 1930.)

mammals. The cranial capacity of modern man is 1200–1500 cc, as against the 350–450 cc of the chimpanzee, and brain size undoubtedly affects intelligence and the ability to learn. Many other characteristics of the head are peculiarly human: the comparatively vertical face, the great reduction in the projection of the jaws, the distinct chin, the prominent nose with its elongated tip, the outwardly rolled mucous membrane of the lips, the rolled margin of the ears. And then of course there is the peculiar distribution of hair, or lack of hair. Mostly we can only guess about the significance of these differences.

Man also differs markedly from the apes in having greatly reduced canine teeth, no more prominent than the premolars and incisors on either side. Since the time of Darwin, scientists have thought that the reduction of the canine teeth might be related to tool using: that man with a club did not need his teeth for offense or defense; or, contrariwise that lacking large canines, man needed a club.

Behavioral Characteristics

Man is unique among the primates in being a predatory, carnivorous animal. To be sure, many groups of modern men are primarily or exclusively vegetarian, but only because they are able to prepare seeds, tubers, and other vegetative materials by cooking with fire. Without fire, man's vegetable diet would be limited to fruits, nuts, and similar special plant products. On the other hand, man can digest all kinds of meat—molluscs, insects, fish, and meat from fellow-mammals—without cooking. Even if we did not have the evidence of the fossil record, we could deduce that man became a hunter before he had learned to master fire.

Man is also a highly social animal, and he is understandable only in terms of his social relationships. Man, as a solitary individual, is basically helpless, despite his vaunted intelligence. If we try to visualize the life of the human animal in the Old Stone Age, we realize that only cooperating groups could catch needed animal food or ward off enemies such as the big cats.

Many kinds of animals show social behavior in the sense that different individuals of the same species act cooperatively for special or varied purposes. The most elaborate societies, aside from the human species, are

Fig. 1-2. (A) Man's posture and leg-arm length ratio vs. those of a great ape. (B) Man's vertical spine and relatively large cranium vs. the ape's forward-thrusting spinal column and smaller cranium. (C) Man's small canine teeth vs. the ape's giant canines. (D) Man's foot vs. ape's foot.

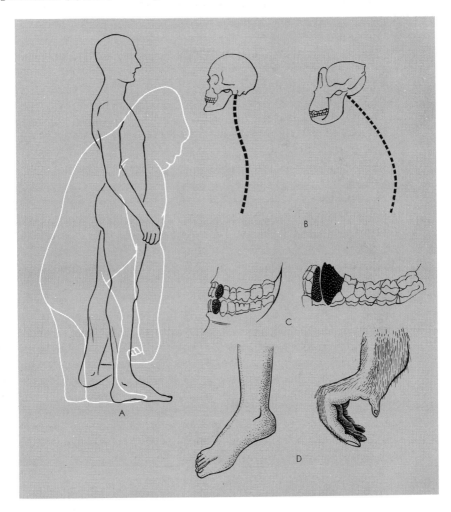

those of the insects. But insect societies are quite different from those of vertebrates, in that they are based primarily on purely instinctive behavior; and even though a particular termite, ant, or bee colony may be composed of many thousands of individuals, they are all members of a single family, consisting of a mother (the queen) and her multitudinous offspring. Comparisons between insect societies and vertebrate societies are only analogies; the sometimes striking similarities are the consequence of quite different evolutionary histories.

There is a wide variety of social behavior in different vertebrates, as is reflected in the words we use for group labels: school, herd, flock, pack, and so forth. The study and analysis of such social interaction constitute a rapidly growing field of biological research.*

Man is a mammal and we can best understand the development of human social behavior by looking at comparable behavior in other mammals. There are three basic classes of individuals within any mammal species: males, females, and young. If we consider social behavior to be a continuing interaction among individuals of a species, we thus have six major kinds of interactions: male-female, female-young, young-young, female-female, male-male, and male-young. With mammals, female-young interaction is universal and inevitable, since the young are dependent on the mother until weaned. There must also be at least periodic male-female interaction, since fertilization is internal. Young-young interaction is almost equally inevitable, since several young are born at a time with most mammals, and where birth is single, a new infant is generally born before the previous one has become completely independent.

In many mammals, a single male may be associated with several females and with their young, forming a polygynous family. The rarest form of association involves several males, females, and young, and in it all six types of possible cooperative interaction must occur if the group is to function smoothly. This sort of social grouping, which occurs in a few mammal groups, including the canines (dogs, wolves, etc.) and the primates, is especially interesting in its bearing on the origins of human behavior. It is difficult to imagine how the complications of language communication could have developed except within fairly large cooperating bands, bands larger than the nuclear family. This intragroup cooperation and communication surely form the essence of purely human behavior.

Man has another even more unusual behavioral characteristic: the long period from birth to sexual maturity. The human infant is completely dependent on adults for from 6 to 8 years, the ape infant for perhaps 2 years, most monkeys for only 1 year (Fig. 1-3). Man reaches puberty at about 14 years and full adult powers at about 20; the corresponding figures

* See in this series, V. G. Dethier and E. Stellar, *Animal Behavior*, 2nd ed., p. 106ff. (Englewood Cliffs, N. J.: Prentice-Hall, 1964).

Fig. 1-3. A baby chimpanzee develops more rapidly than a human infant. (Pictures and data on chimps, courtesy Yerkes Regional Primate Research Center.)

(A) One-day-old chimp: can maintain grasp on toy. Human: can clasp ring at 8 weeks.[1] (B) One-month-old chimp: can sit with minimal support. Human: can sit alone briefly at 25 weeks.[2] (C) Two-month-old chimp: can track a moving object with eyes and can creep forward short distances. Human: can follow a small moving ball with eyes at 12 weeks[1] and can crawl or somehow progress across room toward distant object at 7.3 months.[2] (D) Four-month-old chimp: can sit upsupported. Human: can sit alone for several minutes at 6.2 months.[2] (E) Seven-month-old chimp: can stand unsupported. Human: can stand alone for several moments at 10.7 months.[2] (F) Ten-month-old chimp: can locomote on all fours. Human: can walk alone at 12 months.[2]

[1] Yale Psycho-Clinic, Yale University.
[2] C. Anderson Aldrich and Mildred A. Norval, "Development as a Product of Learning and Growth," in Jerome M. Seidman, ed., *The Child: A Book of Readings* (New York: Holt, Rinehart and Winston, 1958).

for the great apes are about 8 and 12. Mammals other than primates generally show even more rapid developmental rates. This slow human development, taking place within a social group, provides the behavioral basis for culture, for during the long period, the adults can teach and the young can learn. The extrasomatic inheritance of culture requires both transmitting and receiving mechanisms, teaching and learning; the study of these is the crux of a large part of the science of psychology.

Cultural Characteristics

Man may be defined facetiously as a "featherless biped." But when we try to formulate a scientific definition, we tend to use cultural rather than physical or behavioral terms. We say that man is peculiar because he has language—has developed symbols that make abstract thought possible— or because he makes tools, or because he uses fire.

Human language is in some ways similar to, but in other ways vastly different from, other kinds of animal communication. We simply have no idea about its evolutionary history, though many people have speculated about its possible origins. There is, for instance, the "bow-wow" theory, that language started from attempts to imitate animal sounds. Or the "ding-dong" theory, that it arose from natural sound-producing responses. Or the "pooh-pooh" theory, that it began with violent outcries or exclamations.

We have no way of knowing whether the kinds of men represented by the earliest fossils could talk or not. The languages of living men all seem to be about equally complex, equally remote from the signal cries of apes, monkeys, or other animals. Some living peoples, such as the Australian aborigines, have simple material cultures; others, Europeans, for instance, have complex cultures; but we cannot show any relation between the evolution of material culture and the evolution of language. There are thousands of kinds of languages spoken in the world today, and the linguistic experts can trace trends of orderly change within them. Yet none of these throw light on the origin or evolution of language, only on its change and diversification.

Language does not leave fossils, at least not until it has become written. We do find fossil tools, however, which give us clues to the evolution of culture. Tool-using is not unique to man; some insects and vertebrates also have this ability. Tool-making is not unique either, since some monkeys and apes may break off branches to use as sticks. Man's uniqueness is in *the making of tools in accord with a predetermined plan or pattern.* Stones that were obviously shaped for some particular purpose by chipping occur in deposits that date from early in the Pleistocene period. Animals with this essential human characteristic, then, have been around for several hundred thousand years.

The use of fire is more difficult to determine than the habit of shaping tools. There is clear evidence of hearths in the caves at Choukoutien, where Peking man was found, that are thought to date from about the middle of the Pleistocene. But it is more convenient to use tools, rather than fire or language, for drawing the line between man and not-man.

CAPABILITY AND ACHIEVEMENT

When we look about us, the difference between man and other animals seems enormous. Man, with his culture, has spread all over the world, has learned to adapt to the most diverse climates and habitats. He has drastically altered the landscape of large parts of the earth. The canyons of Manhattan may be trivial when compared with the Grand Canyon of the Colorado, but the canyons of Manhattan still are awe-inspiring, and they were built by the efforts of a quite puny animal in a very few years. They are products of the human mind, a mind that seems very different from anything else we can find in nature.

We tend, as scientists, philosophers, or artists, to be impressed with this achievement when we look at man. Because of this, we tend to look at man himself as something quite different from anything else in the system of nature. Certainly biology becomes hopelessly inadequate when we set out to study the human achievement. But, as Harry Harlow has pointed out: * "The probability that a relatively small intellectual gain by man over the anthropoid apes would make possible the development of symbolic language and also culture is given small consideration. It is a common error to fail to differentiate between capability and achievement. Thus, the fledgling swallow a few days before it can fly differs little in anatomical and physiological capacity from the swallow capable of sustained flight, but from the point of view of achievement the two are separated by what appears to be an abysmal gulf."

One problem of biology and psychology, then, is to determine and describe the shift in capability that enabled man to begin the record of human achievement. This is the key problem of human evolution. We are far from being able to outline the precise evolutionary steps that led to the phenomenon of man as we know him, but we are constantly gaining in understanding. Two approaches have been particularly fruitful: comparative studies of the behavior of living animals, and the study of the fragmentary record of human fossils and artifacts. In the next chapter we shall look at the first approach, describing man's closest living relatives, the primates, and placing particular stress on primate behavior. Then, in the following chapter, we shall examine the historical record of human evolution.

* "The Evolution of Learning" in *Behavior and Evolution*, Anne Roe and G. G. Simpson, eds. (New Haven: Yale University Press, 1958) p. 278.

The Primates

CHAPTER TWO

To reconstruct the evolutionary history of any organism or group of organisms, we have three rather different approaches at our command. These might be called the historical, the comparative, and the analytic methods. The historical method is the only one that gives us direct evidence, in the form of fossil remains, from the past. The trouble is that the fossil record is very incomplete and is dependent on the accidents of preservation, and it mostly represents only one aspect of life, the anatomical. We must put flesh on the bones, and, what is even more difficult, judge habits from bones and thus deduce the way of life of the fossil. With man, we have tools as well as bones, and the tools can be considered a fossil record of human habits. Still the record is fragmentary, for the wooden instruments, the skins, the fibers that were surely used by early man have rarely been preserved.

The historical record thus gives us a tantalizingly inadequate collection of facts which we can supplement by comparative and analytic study. But the fossils are facts, and suppositions from other lines of study must always fit this documentary evidence.

Deductions from comparative study are hazardous, but nevertheless interesting and instructive. A wide variety of animal types has survived into the modern world, some of them apparently with little change from very ancient times. By comparing several existing forms, we can make deductions about their common ancestors and reconstruct their possible history. We must always remember, however, that no living form is directly ancestral to any other living form. Living apes are not the ancestors of living men; but by comparing monkeys, apes, and men, we can get some insight into their possible evolutionary histories.

The analytic method is most hazardous of all. By studying man as we see him now, with vestigial parts left over from his past, with traces of long-useless behavior, with a developmental pattern from embryo to adult, we can venture guesses as to how he got the way he is. The results of such study are never more than guesses—even though they may be informed guesses.

We shall look at the fossil record of the hominids in the next chapter. In the present chapter we shall look at man's surviving cousins of various degrees, the primates, not only because they may advance our knowledge of our family tree, but because they are interesting in themselves. After all, no part of a zoo is more popular than the monkey house, and whatever our ancestors may have been like, it seems clear that there is a lot of monkey still left with us.

PRIMATE CLASSIFICATION *

Zoologists now include in the primate order not only apes, monkeys, and lemurs, but also the tree shrews, loris, galagos, and tarsiers. Clear diagnostic characters for this diverse group are not easy to find. In general, the hands and feet are either adapted for climbing, or clearly derived from forms so adapted. There is a clavicle, or collar bone. The digits are freely mobile, and either the thumb or big toe or both are opposable. Some or all of the fingers and toes have flattened nails instead of claws. Usually there are only two mammae, and usually only one young is born at a time.

The number of living primates, compared with other mammal orders, is not large. Almost all of them are tropical, and many of them are rare and little known. But the literature about them is enormous and the opinions are many about how they should be classified. Since man is a primate, the whole order tends to get out of perspective, and the classification even of tarsiers and lemurs takes on emotional elements. G. G. Simpson, the well-known paleontologist, in a survey of the classification of all of the mammals, living and fossil, uses the following system for the primates:

* For a discussion of animal classification, see E. D. Hanson, *Animal Diversity,* 2nd ed. (Englewood Cliffs, N. J.: Prentice-Hall, 1964).

Order Primates
  Suborder Prosimii
    Infraorder Lemuriformes
      Superfamily Tupaioidea
        Family Tupaiidae, tree shrews
      Superfamily Lemuroidea
        Family Lemuridae, lemurs
        Family Indridae, lemurs, indris
      Superfamily Daubentonioidea
        Family Daubentoniidae, aye-ayes
    Infraorder Lorisiformes
      Family Lorisidae, lorises, pottos, galagos
    Infraorder Tarsiiformes
      Family Tarsiidae, tarsiers
  Suborder Anthropoidea
    Superfamily Ceboidea
      Family Cebidae, New World monkeys
      Family Callithricidae, marmosets
    Superfamily Cercopithecoidea
      Family Cercopithecidae, Old World monkeys, baboons
    Superfamily Hominoidea
      Family Pongidae, apes
      Family Hominidae, fossil and living men

THE PROSIMIANS

The Prosimians include a rather miscellaneous group of animals that shed considerable light on the evolution of the higher primates. The fossil record of the primates is the poorest of that of any mammal order. Apparently primates have always been tropical, and largely forest, animals with habits that would only rarely lead to fossilization.

The primates are thought to have developed from the insectivores very early in mammalian evolution. One living group, the tree shrews (Tupaiidae) of the Orient and East Indies, shows characteristics that lead some students to class them with the insectivores; others place them with the primates. The Tupaiids are small, squirrel-like arboreal animals that differ from other primates in having claws rather than nails, but that also have other characteristics similar to those of the lemurs.

The living lemurs and the related aye-ayes, which Simpson classifies into two superfamilies, three families, and ten genera, are found only on the island of Madagascar. Tropical Madagascar has been separated from the continental land masses all through the Tertiary, so that it forms a sort of museum of Eocene mammals that have been protected from competition with more modern mammal types. Since a number of Eocene fossils from both North America and Europe have characteristics similar to the Madagascar lemurs, there is no doubt that they once represented a widespread group.

The ten genera of lemurs differ considerably in behavior. They are mostly arboreal, though many of them forage on the ground, with quad-

Fig. 2-1 The ring-tailed lemur of Madagascar (Lemur catta). (New York Zoological Society Photo.)

Fig. 2-2. A Congo potto, one of the prosimians (Perodicticus potto). (New York Zoological Society Photo.)

rupedal locomotion. One species, *Lemur catta* (Fig. 2-1), is primarily a ground dweller, playing a role similar to that of the African baboons. The lemurs, like monkeys, tend to be omnivorous, but a few, like a few monkey species, feed on leaves and buds. Many of them are easily kept in captivity. Usually only one young is born at a time. Observations on lemur behavior in the wild are scattered and not very detailed. They are said generally to be social, moving in groups of 10 to 20 individuals, but also to fight among themselves; there are, however, no careful studies of territorial behavior or social organization for lemur bands.

Two other prosimian groups are generally recognized: the lorises and the tarsiers. The infraorder *Lorisiformes* includes the bush babies, or galagos, of tropical Africa, the lorises, or "slow lemurs," of tropical Asia, and the pottos (Fig. 2-2) of Africa. They are all small, furry animals, and bush babies, at least, are popular as pets. Most species are nocturnal, making observations on behavior in the wild difficult, and not much is known about them.

There is only one living species of tarsier, *Tarsius spectrum* of the East Indies, but many Eocene fossils from Europe and North America are assigned to the group, so that it must once have been a common and widespread primate type.

NEW WORLD MONKEYS

The monkeys of the New World tropics and those of the Old World are only distantly related; they have had separate evolutionary histories for a very long time. It seems likely that the New World monkeys evolved from a tarsioid

15

or lemuroid stock that reached America in the Eocene or Paleocene, though the scarcity of fossils makes it difficult to be sure of the history of the group.

The most obvious and consistent difference between the two monkey groups lies in the form of the nose. In New World monkeys, the nostrils are separated by a wide partition, and consequently open sideways. Because of this, they are called *platyrrhine* or "flat-nosed" monkeys. The Old World monkeys and apes have narrow nasal septa, so that the nostrils open downward, the *catarrhine* condition. All the New World monkeys have tails, and in many the tail is prehensile. No Old World monkey has a prehensile tail, and in the apes the tail is absent. The Old World monkeys have ishial callosites, naked and often brightly colored areas on the buttocks, which are never present in New World monkeys, who also lack the cheek pouches that are present in most of the Old World forms.

The New World monkeys, or Ceboids, include a variety of different types, a fact that has led some authors to classify them in as many as seven distinct families. Simpson's system of placing them in two families, the *Cebidae* proper, and the *Callithricidae,* or marmosets, seems more reasonable, however (Figs. 2-3 and 2-4).

The marmosets are small, fragile-looking animals of the tropical American rain forest. They differ from the Cebids in many details of anatomy, most sharply in having two instead of three molar teeth on each side of both jaws. They are sometimes kept as pets, but little is known about their habits in the wild. They are generally considered to be less intelligent than the Cebids, and they are the only monkeys that habitually bear two or more offspring at a time. Some students consider them to be "primitive" survivors of the line ancestral to the Cebids, while others think they are a "specialized" or even "degenerate" offshoot from the Cebids.

The tropical American Cebid monkeys are interesting animals from many points of view. There are twelve genera, the species of which differ from each other greatly in appearance, habits, and temperament. This diversity has presumably evolved within the tropical American forest from some primitive, early Eocene primate stock. None of them has achieved large, ape-like size—rumors of large, wild primates in South America have never been substantiated. They all remain arboreal, but they have achieved a high degree of intelligence and some of them, in experimental problem-solving situations, do as well as the great apes. They are also highly social animals, and studies of their group behavior have increased our understanding of the social behavior of the primates.

A classical study of primate behavior in the wild was made by C. R. Carpenter on one of the Cebids, the howler monkey (*Alouatta*) (Fig. 2-5),

Fig. 2-3 (Left) A New World monkey, the capuchin (Cebus apella). **(New York Zoological Society Photo.)**

Fig. 2-4. (Right) A New World marmoset (Hapale jacchus). **(New York Zoological Society Photo.)**

on Barro Colorado Island in the Panama Canal Zone.* This island was formed when the Chagres Valley was flooded to make Gatun Lake in the course of the construction of the Panama Canal. It was set aside in 1923 as a natural history reserve for the study of rain forest fauna and flora, and no hunting has been allowed since that time. Many of the animals have lost their extreme shyness, so that it is possible to carry out behavior studies under particularly favorable conditions.

The howler monkeys are the largest of the Cebids, in terms of body weight, and they are perhaps the noisiest of all animals. The hyoid bone of the throat is enlarged into a box-like resonator, and the whole larynx is greatly developed. It has been estimated that the roar of an individual can be heard for three miles, and a clan of howlers can make a really formidable racket. They regularly greet the dawn with roars, and the morning choruses remain a vivid impression with anyone who has lived in remote parts of the tropical American forest.

* C. R. Carpenter, "A Field Study of the Behavior and Social Relations of Howling Monkeys," *Comparative Psychological Monographs,* vol. 10, no. 2.

Fig. 2-5. A New World monkey, the howler (Alouatta palliata). (New York Zoological Society Photo.)

Dr. Carpenter spent nearly a year on Barro Colorado Island, going out to observe the behavior of the monkey clans every day. He found 23 separate bands of these monkeys on the island, which has an area of a little less than 4000 acres. The largest band included 35 monkeys and the smallest 4, and he estimated the total howler population of the island to be about 400. The average band consisted of 3 adult males, 7 adult females, and associated young. There were a few "bachelor" males unattached to any band.

Carpenter selected one band of 26 monkeys and mapped its movements every day for a month. From this and from subsequent less regular observations, he found that the movements of the band were confined to a definite territory of about 300 acres. The monkeys tended to spend the night in particular "lodge trees" and to follow the same pathways through the trees from one part of the territory to another. There was very little overlap between the territory of this band and the territories of neighboring bands, and Carpenter concluded that each monkey band on the island had its characteristic range.

"Territory" in biology is defined as an area defended by an individual, pair, or social group of a particular species against other individuals of the same species. An area that is regularly occupied but apparently not defended is generally referred to as a "home range." Carpenter found that the howler bands tended to avoid each other, but that they would approach one another on the margins of their territories and start a vigorous vocal "battle" that would continue until one band or the other retired. Individual "bachelor" males that tried to join bands were also rejected, or accepted only after prolonged advances. The howler behavior, then, was clearly territorial, even though the territorial pattern was probably constantly but gradually shifting, and even though in some cases it seemed that the ranges of different bands overlapped considerably.

Territorial behavior in the living primates is of interest in connection

18

with human evolution. Early human and prehuman fossils frequently indicate that death was violent and at the hands of fellow hominids, which would be natural if we assume that these early men showed social and territorial behavior something like that of the howler monkeys; only these early men, instead of simply yelling at each other, got into physical combat with weapons. We can still speculate whether traces of territorial behavior linger on in living men. Food-gathering and hunting tribes, like those of Australia and the Malay forests, certainly often show territorial patterns similar to those of the monkeys.

Carpenter paid particular attention to social organization within the howler bands. He found no evidence of "dominance" or "leadership" by particular individuals; the howlers seemed to have a communal organization. When a band was on the move, one of the adult males was usually in the lead, but not necessarily the same male each time; and sometimes one of the females would be leading. He also found no evidence of sexual jealousy among the males: Females in heat took the initiative in approaching males. Care of infants and young was entirely in the hands of the females, except that adult males would occasionally play with the young and would show alarm and distress (not very helpfully) when a young monkey accidentally fell. There seemed to be relatively little teaching or coaching of the young.

Unfortunately, we know nothing about the behavior of howler monkeys under laboratory conditions. They are difficult to keep alive in captivity, and no studies have been made of their intelligence or learning ability. They are generally considered to be less intelligent than some of the other New World monkeys, but there is no experimental basis for this opinion. On the other hand, none of the other species has been so carefully studied in the wild, though it seems probable that all the Cebids (except possibly the night monkey, *Aotus*) show similar communal and territorial behavior.

The award for intelligence among the New World monkeys goes to the capuchins, the monkeys of the organ grinders, species of the genus *Cebus*. These monkeys are not easy to work with in the laboratory because they are both intelligent and willful—not easily disciplined. It is clear, however, that *Cebus* monkeys are as adept as the great apes in using tools and solving problems. One *Cebus* studied by Heinrich Klüver of the University of Chicago would even "make" tools, by tearing off pieces of newspaper and rolling them into makeshift rakes, or by breaking off pieces of sticks.

OLD WORLD MONKEYS

The Old World monkeys, in the classification of G. G. Simpson, are placed in sixteen genera divided among two subfamilies. One of these, the Cercopithecinae, includes the baboons, macaques, and their relatives, many of them ground-living and all except the macaques purely African. The other subfamily, the Colobinae, is purely arboreal and includes five Oriental genera (the various langurs and the proboscis monkeys) and one African genus, *Colobus*. The Old World monkeys are more uniform in anatomy than the New World forms, as is shown by Simpson's division of the one group into two subfamilies and the other into six.

The best known of the Old World monkeys is the Indian macaque or rhesus monkey (genus *Macaca*), so common in laboratories and zoos (Fig. 2-6). It is a major pest of gardens and fields in India and is trapped in large numbers for export to experimental laboratories all over the world. When psychologists or physiologists refer to "the monkey," they generally mean the rhesus monkey. Rhesus monkeys can be bred fairly easily in captivity—which is not true of most primates—so that their behavior can be studied from infancy to old age. Many studies have been made of their learning ability, perception, and discrimination. They show a much greater ability to solve complex problems than any other common laboratory animal, though their performance is not as good as that of *Cebus* or the chimpanzee.

Unfortunately, we do not have correspondingly detailed studies of their behavior as wild animals. They are clearly social, living in bands that may

Fig. 2-6. (Left) An Old World monkey (Macaca irus). **(New York Zoological Society Photo.)**

Fig. 2-7. (Right) An African baboon (Mandrillus sphinx). **(New York Zoological Society Photo.)**

Fig. 2-8. A gibbon (Hylobates lar). (**New York Zoological Society Photo.**)

include as many as 150 individuals. Both rhesus monkeys and baboons apparently show territorial behavior. In captivity both rhesus and baboon groups have a dominance hierarchy, or peck-order, with one adult male dominant; it may be, however, that dominance and sexual jealousy are more striking under captive conditions than in the wild. This clearly is the case with African baboons (Fig. 2-7).*

THE GREAT APES

GIBBONS. The various species of gibbons *(Hylobates* and *Symphalangus)* of Southeast Asia are generally classified apart from the other great apes as a separate subfamily or sometimes family. They are the smallest of the apes—the adults stand about three feet high—and they are by far the best arboreal acrobats, with long arms that reach the ground when an animal stands erect (Fig. 2-8). Carpenter made careful field studies of one species of gibbon in Thailand. He found that they lived in monogamous families consisting of an adult male and female with one or more young. Each family lived within a definite territory and when two families approached on the borders of their territories, unfriendly and aggressive be-

* "The Social Life of Baboons" by S. L. Washburn and Ide Vore in the *Scientific American,* June, 1961.

21

Fig. 2-9. **Orang-utans** (Pongo pygmaeus). **(New York Zoological Society Photo.)**

havior was often observed, though this did not seem to lead to actual fighting.

ORANG-UTAN. Only one species of orang exists *(Pongo pygmaeus),* and it is found in Sumatra and Borneo. Very little is known of its habits in the wild. It is more arboreal than either the gorilla or the chimpanzee, but because of its considerable weight (averaging 81 pounds for females and 165 pounds for males), it reportedly proceeds through the trees with great caution (Fig. 2-9). The males are said to be essentially solitary, though groups of two or three females with their young may live together. Stories of animals raised in captivity by residents of Sumatra and Borneo sound like similar stories of chimps in terms of affection for humans and intelligent actions. But orangs have not been raised under the eyes of careful psychological observers.

GORILLA (genus *Gorilla*). There are two forms of gorilla in Africa: a mountain type in the vicinity of Lake Edward and Lake Kivu; and a lowland form in the deep rain forest of the Cameroons and the Congo. Both are big animals, the males weighing as much as 450 pounds (becoming even heavier in the confined life of zoos) and standing six feet high or more; the females are somewhat smaller (Fig. 2-10). The size, strength, and uncertain temper of captive gorillas make psychological experiments difficult, and few have been attempted.

It was long thought that the ferocity and wariness of gorillas would make careful study of behavior in the wild impossible, and up until recently all attempts at such study produced disappointing results. In 1960, however, George B. Schaller of the University of Wisconsin discovered that by going into gorilla country alone and unarmed he could quite readily establish contact with the animals and observe their daily actions in detail. He has reported the results of this study in a fascinating book.*

Gorillas look fierce; and the males, at least, will defend themselves vigorously if attacked. But Schaller found that in their home forests they were placid, peaceable animals, secure from any enemy except armed men and possibly leopards. They live in social groups including two to 30 individuals—the average for ten groups in one region was 17 animals. One adult male is the leader, and there is a clear dominance hierarchy among the males; but Schaller observed no fighting except, rarely, a certain amount of squabbling among the females. Apparently the dominant male is not sexually jealous of the other males in the group, and the choice of mate depends on the inclinations of the particular female—though in general the gorillas show remarkably little interest in sex, and sexual activity is rare.

Each gorilla group tends to stay within a particular area—a home range covering 10 to 15 square miles. They are not, however, territorial in the strict sense of that word, since the range of a particular group is not defended against intrusion by outsiders. Several groups, in fact, may range over the same area, and groups may build nests and pass the night within a few hundred yards of each other quite peaceably. Members of different groups, however, do not freely intermingle and when two groups are close, the leaders sometimes show a form of conflict by attempting to stare each other down, one or the other eventually giving way. A direct stare is a form of aggression among gorillas, like the howling of Carpenter's Panama monkeys. The behavior of

Fig. 2-10. A gorilla (Gorilla gorilla). (New York Zoological Society Photo.)

* George B. Schaller, *The Mountain Gorilla; Ecology and Behavior* (Chicago: University of Chicago Press, 1963).

Fig. 2-11. A chimpanzee (Pan troglodytes). (New York Zoological Society Photo.)

these animals, then, sheds little light on the possible origin of the damaging intergroup conflict that has so long characterized the human species. Gorillas and other apes are vegetarian, while the evidence indicates that the human line has been predatory for a very long time: perhaps this is the basis of human ferocity.

CHIMPANZEE. There are several varieties or, possibly, species of chimps: a white-faced, a black-faced, a bald-headed, and a pygmy form. All are from tropical Africa and all are classified in the genus *Pan*. Infant chimps adapt readily to human companionship, unlike infant gorillas, which tend to be sullen and suspicious. The result is that chimps are popular zoo animals (Fig. 2-11), and quite a number of chimps have been raised under circumstances where detailed studies could be made of their behavioral development. In 1930, R. M. Yerkes established the Laboratories of Primate Biology at Orange Park, Florida; chimpanzees have been the object of special study there ever since. The result has been a large accumulation of information about the behavior and physiology of this most man-like of living animals.

For animals in the wild, we have as yet no published study giving details of behavior comparable with those observed by Schaller with gorillas. It is clear, however, that the behavior of the two apes differs in many respects. For one thing, the lighter-weight chimpanzees are much more arboreal in their habits than are the gorillas. For another, it seems that the chimps have a much looser social organization. One observer (Vernon Reynolds, quoted by Schaller) found between 65 and 75 chimpanzees ranging over an area of six to eight square miles of forest in Uganda; but changes occurred daily in the grouping of these animals. Sometimes several males would roam together; sometimes mothers with infants were found by themselves; sometimes small bands comparable with those of gorillas would form, only to disperse and regroup after a few days.

Several chimps have been raised in households where they were given the same care and attention as human children. Their performance under these circumstances is remarkable: They learn to manipulate household gadgets and to carry out many kinds of complicated actions. They outstrip human children up to the time when communication through language becomes dominant. The apes learn to respond to language, to a wide variety of words, but all efforts to try to make them speak have failed. One infant, with the greatest effort, was taught to say whispered approximations of "mama," "papa," and "cup"; but that is all. This failure apparently is not a consequence of anatomy: The infant apes just do not go through the sound-imitating and sound-producing stage that characterizes every human child. Schaller noted this same absence of sound-imitativeness in the play of wild gorilla juveniles.

Human
Evolution

CHAPTER THREE

When Darwin published the *Descent of Man,* in 1871, he built his case for human evolution entirely on evidence from living men and living primates, and he thought that "the great break in the organic chain" between apes and men might never be bridged because of the imperfect nature of the fossil record. His book did, however, create the climate of opinion in which the importance of finding "missing links" became widely recognized, and people became alert to the possible significance of any old human bones they might come across.

Actually, the first of the important human fossils was found in 1856 in one of the grottoes along the little vale called Neanderthal, near Düsseldorf, Germany. A local school-teacher, Johann Karl Fuhlrott, collected the bone fragments revealed by workers in a quarry and recognized them as belonging to some ancient, brutish sort of man. A professor at Bonn, Hermann Schaafhausen, agreed with Fuhlrott, and the two of them presented their discovery at a meeting of eminent scientists in 1857. Neanderthal man was, at least temporarily, demolished at that meeting. The great anatomist Rudolf Virchow declared the skeleton to be pathological. He claimed it belonged to an individual who had been born with a skull deformity, who in youth had suffered from rickets with consequent damage to leg bones and pelvis, and who in old age had suffered from arthritis.

The argument over the meaning of the Neanderthal skeleton continued. A skull that had been found in Gibraltar in 1848 was presented to the Royal College of Surgeons in 1868 and presently recognized as being of the Neanderthal type. But Virchow's verdict was not completely discredited until after 1880, when various Neanderthal remains were discovered under conditions that left no question about their antiquity.

The Neanderthal controversy illustrates something that happens in science occasionally—a new discovery or new idea is rejected for a time because the weight of authority is against it. Scientists are human, and even great scientists can be very wrong. Virchow was a major scientist, even though he was mistaken about Neanderthal man; his contributions to anatomy and medicine were numerous and important. We forget, of course, the many cases in which authority was right and the new idea wrong. The important thing in science is that authority, as such, cannot prevail in the long run against accumulating evidence.

Another not infrequent phenomenon in science is the man who becomes obsessed with an idea and carries on under adverse circumstances to eventual success. An example in the history of human evolution is provided by Eugene Dubois. Dubois, while a medical student in Amsterdam, decided to dedicate himself to the search for fossil man. He reasoned that Java was the proper place to look, because Pleistocene fossil beds were known to exist there and because he suspected that early human evolution had probably taken place in the Asiatic tropics.

Dubois got a job as an army surgeon in the colonial service and was soon off to Java; once there, he spent all the time he could spare exploring the fossil beds. The extraordinary thing is that almost immediately he found an ape-like tooth and then, within ten feet, some more teeth and the top of a skull, too large for an ape and too small for a man. A year later he came upon the thighbone of a man now known as Java man and described by Dubois in 1894 as *Pithecanthropus erectus* (Fig. 3-1).

Fig. 3-1. The skull of modern man (left) and a reconstructed skull of Pithecanthropus erectus **(right).**

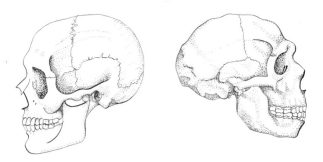

Again there were endless controversies over the significance of the find. Dubois tired of the arguments and returned with his bones to Holland, where for nearly 20 years he would allow no one to examine the fossils. Then, when the learned world had come to accept *Pithecanthropus,* Dubois emerged again and permitted fellow scientists to study his fossils. But, curiously, he himself had now changed his mind; when everyone else had come to believe that the Java find represented an early man, Dubois maintained that it was no man at all, but a giant gibbon.

A third, and fortunately very rare, event in science—fraud—is illustrated by Piltdown man. In 1908 a British lawyer and amateur archaeologist, Charles Dawson, discovered a fragment of a human skull in a gravel bed, and three years later found another fragment. He took his pieces to Sir Arthur Smith Woodward, the geologist of the British Museum, who thought Dawson might have found parts of a peculiar human fossil. The two of them continued the search, and turned up half of a lower jaw. In 1912 they announced their discovery, Woodward naming the fossil *Eoanthropus dawsoni.* The skull fragments were human, the jaw fragment ape-like; but a good part of the scientific world never would admit that the two could go together, though no one suspected fraud.

The idea that the Piltdown fragments might be a hoax finally occurred to a British anthropologist, J. S. Weiner. He and two of his colleagues, Kenneth Oakley and W. E. Le Gros Clark, undertook a very thorough study of the fragments, including an analysis of the fluorine content (fluorine gradually leaches out of fossil bones). They published their findings in 1953, providing beyond any doubt that the jaw fragment was from a modern ape, probably an orang-utan, carefully treated to make it look like a fossil. The skull fragment, however, was a true fossil. The circumstances of the hoax remain obscure, but a difficult problem in human evolution was solved, because the association of the ape-like jaw with a modern type human skull never had made sense.*

In the late 1920's and early 1930's, a series of man-like fossils was found in cave deposits near Choukoutien in China, 42 miles from the city of Peking (now Peiping) (Fig. 3-2). These were the remains of what has come to be called "Peking Man" or *Sinanthropus.* In subsequent years a variety of hominid fossils have been discovered, mostly in Africa, and we are gradually recovering more material on ancient man than Darwin had ever hoped for. These do not, however, form a neat chain of links leading from ancient ape to modern man. They cannot be arranged in any single sequence and it appears that a considerable variety of man-like animals lived at different times and places in the Pleistocene. One of these —the kind we know today—eventually won out.

All of the known hominoid or man-like fossils belong to the last of the

---

* This detective story in modern science has been recounted in a book by J. S. Weiner, *The Piltdown Forgery* (New York: Oxford University Press, 1955).

Fig. 3-2. The site where the remains of Sinanthropus were discovered near Peking, the present capital of Communist China. (Courtesy American Museum of National History.)

geological periods, the Pleistocene, which goes back about a million years (Fig. 3-3). These fossils often differ markedly from modern men, but they differ even more from modern apes. Paleontologists and anthropologists are now generally agreed that the human and ape lines have had separate evolutionary histories for a very long time, although the fossil record is not complete enough to indicate exactly how long. Few primate fossils are known from the Pliocene, which preceded the Pleistocene, and none of these throws light on human origins. A primate from the next period, the Miocene, named *Proconsul,* already shows hominoid features and may well have figured in human ancestry. This would give man an evolutionary history distinct from that of the other living primate types for at least 15 million years and probably much longer. The idea of a "missing link" between modern men and living apes can thus be very misleading—the Miocene primates ancestral to both lines were very different from either.

About men and man-like animals in the Pleistocene we are learning more every year. The Pleistocene was short, as geological periods go, and it was also peculiar in having great changes in climate. Four waves of glaciation ground their way across much of North America and Europe, and particular events are usually dated with reference to these glacial and interglacial periods, even though the absolute time range involved remains uncertain.

Chipped or flaked stones are found in Pleistocene deposits of different ages in many parts of the Old World— direct evidence of human activity.

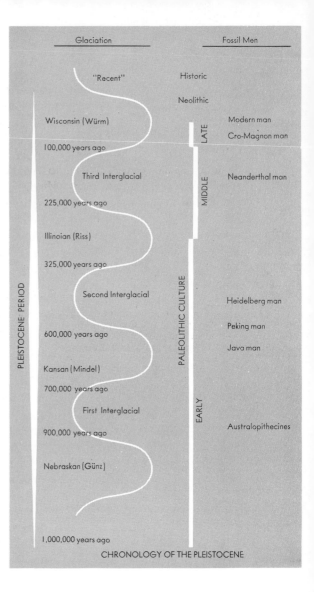

Glaciation		Fossil Men

"Recent" — Historic

Neolithic

Wisconsin (Würm) — LATE — Modern man / Cro-Magnon man

100,000 years ago

Third Interglacial — MIDDLE — Neanderthal man

225,000 years ago

Illinoian (Riss)

325,000 years ago

Second Interglacial — Heidelberg man

600,000 years ago — Peking man

Java man

Kansan (Mindel)

700,000 years ago

First Interglacial — EARLY

900,000 years ago — Australopithecines

Nebraskan (Günz)

1,000,000 years ago

PLEISTOCENE PERIOD

PALEOLITHIC CULTURE

CHRONOLOGY OF THE PLEISTOCENE

Fig. 3-3. Chart of the Pleistocene Epoch, showing the approximate relation of glacial advances to cultural periods and hominid fossils. European names for the four main glacial periods are in parentheses.

Such implements in the New World occur only in late Pleistocene deposits, and no hominoid fossils at all have been found in America. It is thus assumed that man reached America rather late, perhaps 35 or 40 thousand years ago.

Archaeologists have worked out an elaborate classification of different "industries" by studying how the stone tools were made. Each industry is given a name, usually after the place where it was first discovered. Thus the "Chellean industry" derives its name from Chelles-sur-Marne in France, where these distinctive tools were found in gravel pits. Chellean picks and hand axes were made in a distinctive way by knocking off flakes from nodules of flint. Traces of this industry exist in many parts of Europe and date from the second interglacial period. Presumably these implements correspond to a particular way of life, a particular cultural stage in human evolution. But in this and in most other cases, we do not have fossils directly associated with the tools, so we cannot be sure of the physical characters of the man or man-like animal that made them.

The various industries of most of the Pleistocene are classed together by archaeologists as belonging to the Paleolithic period, or "Old Stone Age." We can recognize Early, Middle, and Late stages in the Paleolithic from the different degrees of skill needed to make the tools. More elaborate and better-formed implements have been found, from the time when the last glaciation began to retreat, a time that marks the transition to the "New Stone Age," or Neolithic period. We thus have two different vocabularies for dealing with the sequences in human evolution: One is based on geological and paleontological evidence, on fossils; the other on archaeological evidence, on implements or cultural remains. We have tried to indicate how these correspond in the chart in Fig. 3-3.

Experts differ in the way they classify the various hominid fossils that have been found. There has been a tendency to make a new genus for almost every new fossil—like *Pithecanthropus* for Java man and *Sinanthropus* for Peking man. But this distorts relationships, since the fossil types vary greatly in their similarity to one another and to modern man. For this reason, biologists who have become concerned with human evolution have tried to make the naming of the fossils accord better with the usual practices of animal classification. Thus Theodosius Dobzhansky, the distinguished geneticist, who has written an excellent summary of what we now know about human evolution (cited in the reading list at the end of this book), has classified the known man-like fossils into two genera, five species, and 17 races or subspecies. By this system, Java man and Peking man are considered to represent two races of a single species, which is called *Homo erectus*. Only the African "ape-men" are considered different enough from us to be classified in a separate genus, *Australopithecus*.

THE AUSTRALOPITHECINES

In 1924, Raymond Dart, newly appointed professor of anatomy at the University of Witwatersrand in South Africa, received some boxes of fossils for his growing collection. Among them was an ape-like skull which looked different from that of any known ape—or of any man. Dart decided his skull belonged to an infant "ape-man" and he gave it the scientific name, *Australopithecus africanus,* from *australis,* south, and *pithecus,* ape. Although convinced that he had a "missing link," he got relatively little support from the scientific world, for most anthropologists thought he had some sort of fossil ape, remote from the human line.

In 1936 Robert Broom found a second Australopithecine skull in a lime quarry at Sterkfontein, near Johannesburg. The fossil this time was from an adult, and was obviously similar to the creature found by Dart, but it differed enough in details of tooth structure to lead Broom to classify it as a separate species, which he named *Australopithecus transvaalensis*. It is now considered by Dobzhansky to represent at most a somewhat different race. In 1938, Broom found fragments of another ape-man skull so different that he named it as a separate genus. Discoveries have continued, and now fossil fragments of some dozens of Australopithecine individuals have become recovered from South African localities. In 1959 the British paleontologist L. S. B. Leakey discovered in Tanganyika a particularly interesting fossil Australopithecine, which he named *Zinjanthropus*—though again most students do not consider a distinct generic name to be warranted.

From the structure of the pelvis and from the way the skull is attached to the spinal column, we know that the Australopithecines were fully bipedal and walked upright. They were rather small, averaging perhaps five feet tall, but they had heavy jaws and unusually large teeth, especially the molars and premolars. Isolated giant human teeth have been found in other places, and from the size of these teeth it was once thought that giant forms of man may have roamed the earth in the past. But it now seems more likely that these large teeth belonged to rather small man-like animals.

Were the Australopithecines "men"? This, of course, is a matter of definition. As far as physical structure is concerned, they have been called men from the neck down and apes from the neck up. Their cranial capacity was not much more than that of a chimpanzee; the normal chimp range is about 350–450 cc, that of the Australopithecines 450–550 cc, compared with 1200–1500 cc for modern man. We cannot be sure of their appearance except that they were very low-browed without much of a chin. We do not know whether they were hairy or not, or what their facial features looked like.

We have learned much about their way of life, however, from careful excavations in the Transvaal caves and from Leakey's studies in Tanganyika. Bones associated with the hominid fossils reveal that they hunted many kinds of animals, including baboons and antelope, and it is hard to imagine this kind of hunting except by well-coordinated social groups. Leakey's Tanganyika man, the earliest of them all, clearly used pebble tools, but no stone tools have been found in the somewhat later South African cave deposits. Raymond Dart and his associates, however, are convinced that many of the bones found in the caves were shaped for use as tools, and Dart considers that the Australopithecine way of life was based on the use of bones, teeth and horn—to which he gives the jaw-breaking label "osteodontokeratic culture." Whether they had fire or not we cannot determine. Black materials in the caves, at first thought to be surviving traces of hearths, have turned out to be manganese. Nor do we know whether they could talk, or how developed was their vocal communication system. The nature of some of the bone fractures indicates that they had already acquired the very human habit of occasionally killing each other. If not men, then, they were at least well on the way to becoming men.

JAVA MAN AND PEKING MAN

The hominid type discovered in Java and the one discovered near Peking are generally agreed to be very similar, probably best considered different races of a single species, already near enough to us to be placed in the genus *Homo*. Parts of something like 40 individuals have been recovered from the Choukoutien caves, so that much more is known about Peking man than about the Java hominid.

Peking man, with a cranial capacity averaging around 1000 cc, had considerably more brains than his Australopithecine predecessors. He made various sorts of rather crude tools, and from traces of carbon found in the caves, it appears he knew how to manage fire. Many of the long bones found in the cave have been split open. Since only man can split bones open—to get at the marrow other animals chew the bones—we are forced to conclude that the Old Stone Age men of the Peking caves were addicted to cannibalism.

NEANDERTHAL MAN

About a hundred remains of Neanderthal man have been discovered since Fuhlrott found the first specimen in the valley near Düsseldorf in 1856, and this kind of man must have been prevalent in Europe, the Near East, and neighboring regions for a very long time. He was a man, by any definition: a rather short, stocky fellow, with a brain about as big as that of modern man, but with a rather differently shaped face and skull (Fig. 3-4), which probably gave him something of the brutish appearance cartoonists use in picturing cave men. He fashioned many kinds of tools and sometimes buried his dead, which indicates he was capable of abstract or religious thought.

Neanderthal man was apparently a sort of side line in human evolution, living in southern Europe while modern man was evolving somewhere farther south. He disappeared when the more efficient modern man moved north, perhaps exterminated by this competitor, perhaps partially absorbed by hybridization. Some anthropologists claim to see Neanderthaloid characteristics in living populations and have found, in a collection of skeletons discovered in caves on Mount Carmel in Palestine, evidence of the hybridization process.

MODERN MAN

There is still no consensus among the experts about how the various human and man-like fossils relate to the evolution of the *Homo sapiens* that dominates the earth today. One group believes that modern man may really be

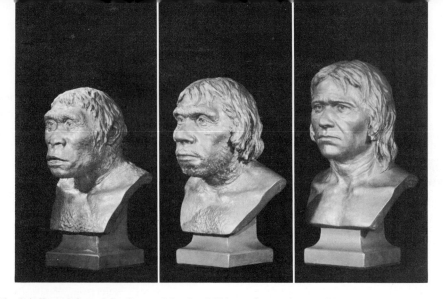

Fig. 3-4. From left to right: Restored heads of Pithecanthropus erectus, **Neander-thal man, and Cro-Magnon man. (Courtesy American Museum of National History.)**

modern and did not reach his present physique (and brain power) until about 50,000 years ago. Others think he may be much older. The trouble is that the *sapiens*-like fossil fragments that might come from middle or early Pleistocene cannot be dated with absolute certainty.

Whether they were direct ancestors or not, the Australopithecine and other fossils at least show us that man-like animals could make and use tools long before they reached the brain capacity of modern man. The highly developed human brain, therefore, may be the consequence, rather than the cause, of culture. Once a man-like animal had started using tools, the forces of natural selection would tend to favor individuals with the greatest ability at making and using them and with the best muscular and neural coordination—in short, individuals with the best brains. This puts a new light on the difference of opinion about human evolution that developed between Darwin and Wallace in the later years of their lives.

THE DARWIN-WALLACE DIFFERENCE

Darwin, as we have seen, based his ideas about the descent of man entirely on the evidence of living apes and men. He did not clearly distinguish between human biology and human culture, which is hardly surprising, since the anthropological study of culture was only beginning in his time. He felt that a progression existed between the most backward and primitive of living people and the most civilized. His one close experience with primitive people, on Tierra del Fuego, left him with a low opinion of their intelligence. True, the gap between ape and Fuegian or Bushman was large, but it did not seem as large to Darwin (Fig. 3-5) as it does to us—or did to Alfred Russell Wallace (Fig. 3-6), the co-discoverer, with Darwin, of the principle of natural selection.

34

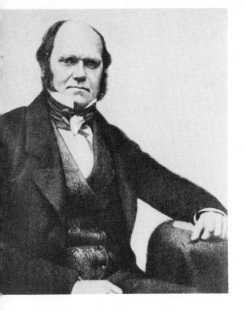

Fig. 3-5. Charles Darwin (1809–1882). (Bettmann Archive.)

Wallace, with his years of living intimately with primitive peoples in the upper Amazon region and in the East Indies and Malaya, came to feel that they were just as intelligent as he or any European and that although these peoples had very different cultures and ways of life, their potentialities were about the same as ours. The gap between all men and any ape is enormous. Wallace could not see how this gap could have been bridged by the process of natural selection. What selective forces in the tropical forests could have developed the potentialities for making steam engines, or composing symphonies—could have led to the development of the human mind? He finally came to the conclusion that the principle of natural selection which Darwin and he had discovered could not apply to human evolutions; that man must be an exception to the orderly operation of biological laws. Darwin, on the other hand, continued to believe firmly that man was a natural phenomenon and that his development was in accordance with natural laws.

Most anthropologists and biologists today consider Wallace to have been right in his view that human nature is essentially the same everywhere, despite man's cultural diversity, and Darwin to have been right in that, for the purposes of science, we must find explanations in terms of natural laws. We can reconcile their difference in terms of the distinction between capability and achievement, as made by Harry Harlow in the quotation in the first chapter, and in terms of what might be called *preadaptation*.

We now know that an Eskimo or an African tribesman, properly trained, can fly an airplane as well as a European and that, with proper materials and knowledge, he could presumably make one, too. We have no evidence

Fig. 3-6. Alfred Russell Wallace (1823–1913). (Brown Brothers.)

of biological evolution in man since the days, thousands of years ago, when Cro-Magnon man made his extraordinary paintings on the cave walls in southern France and Spain (Fig. 3-7). Cro-Magnon man could have made and flown an airplane if his *culture* had reached that evolutionary stage.

If we reverse this problem, we can perhaps understand it better. When modern archaeologists have set themselves the task of learning to chip and shape stone tools, after the fashion of the men of the late Stone Age, they have found that it is not easy and that it takes a highly educated scientist a long time to learn to do a decent job. The coordination of hand and eye, the care and foresight required for shaping a simple stone tool are essentially the same as the coordination and care required to manufacture and manipulate the most complicated gadgets of our civilization. The shift in capability that led to all our vaunted accomplishments started way back with some Australopithecine-like, rather small-brained primate who embarked on a career of tool-making, teaching, and learning, and began accumulating the know-how and tradition, the extrasomatic inheritance, that underlies *cultural evolution.*

Fig. 3-7. A Cro-Magnon painting of a bison, Altamira Cave, Spain: (top) as it appears on the cave wall today; (bottom) a modern copy showing how it probably looked when painted. (Both courtesy American Museum of National History.)

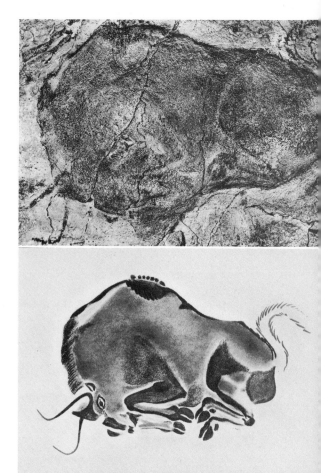

But we still do not know the genetic steps of biological evolution that made the beginning of culture possible. An experimental approach to this mystery is impossible, since we cannot establish breeding populations of people in the laboratory for study, as we can with mice or fruit flies. We can only observe different kinds of living men, hunt diligently for fossils, and then speculate on such information as is available. One hypothesis about human evolution, which may be very wide of the mark but which is nevertheless thought-provoking, involves the theory of *neoteny*.

Neoteny describes the condition in which a species of animal becomes sexually mature before it has attained the normal, physically adult characteristics of that type of animal. The classical case is the Mexican salamander called the *axolotl*. Most salamanders have an aquatic larval stage, with respiration taking place through external gills, followed by an adult stage in which the gills are lost and air-breathing lungs develop. The axolotl has external gills, aquatic habits, and looks like a larval salamander—but it becomes sexually mature and reproduces. It was thought to be a special and peculiar form of salamander until some researchers discovered that under certain conditions (if the animal is fed thyroid extract, for instance) the axolotl transforms into the adult form of an ordinary sort of salamander called *Ambystoma*. The peculiarities of the axolotl were thus seen in a quite new light: The experiments showed how a drastic change in the appearance of an animal at sexual maturity could be brought about by a shift in the timing of physiological events. Some insects and other animals are also known to achieve sexual maturity in larval forms, and this appears to be one possible mechanism of evolutionary change.

An adult man, in many ways, is more similar to a baby ape than to an adult ape. The similarities include the relatively high brain weight, the angle of the head with the trunk, the retarded closure of the sutures between the bones of the skull, the form of the teeth, the flatness of the face, and the hairlessness of the body. Perhaps, then, man, as was first suggested by Bolk in 1926, is a neotenous primate.

One of man's very basic characteristics is the long period of infancy and immaturity, which is essentially controlled by the endocrine gland system. Human evolution must, therefore, have involved changes in these glandular relations that led to the great prolongation of development. The theory of neoteny far from explains all these changes, but it does provide a provocative basis for speculation. And since we generally find the young of other animals more attractive than the adults, it is amusing to think that man may simply be a sort of primate that has permanently lost the ability to grow up.

The Varieties
of Men

CHAPTER FOUR

The tenth edition of the *Systema Naturae* of Carolus Linnaeus is, by universal agreement, the starting point of zoological nomenclature, of the binomial name system used in the classification of animals. The catalog starts with man; *Homo sapiens* is placed at the beginning of the order of primates and the class of mammals. Linnaeus listed four varieties for this species:

Americanus: rufus, cholericus, rectus (red, irascible, upright).

Europaeus: albus, sanguineus, torosus (white, hopeful, brawny).

Asiaticus: luridus, melancholicus, rigidus (yellow, sad, unbending).

Afer: niger, phlegmaticus, laxus (black, calm, lazy).

It is interesting that Linnaeus used geographical names for his four varieties, and that he characterized them by the adjectives designating the four humors of medieval medicine: choleric, sanguine, melancholic, phlegmatic. It makes a nice balanced scheme—except it doesn't work.

There have been endless attempts since the days of Linnaeus to classify the races of man, but no single scheme has become standard. Racial classification has been distorted by racial prejudice, and one group of students would like to solve this problem by completely avoiding the word "race." Yet people are undeniably different, and there is a certain order in the pattern of their physical—biological—differences that ought to be susceptible of description and expression in the language of science.

MAN AS A SPECIES

All living men belong to a single biological species, *Homo sapiens*. "Species" in sexually reproducing organisms is usually defined as a population of similar individuals that actually or potentially interbreed and that are separated from individuals of other similar populations by barriers to breeding. We have to say "actually or potentially" capable of interbreeding because, in fact, individuals in Cuba, for instance, usually have no chance to breed with individuals in Jamaica. In most cases the taxonomist is forced to guess about the status of such geographically separated populations. If he thinks they would interbreed if not separated by some barrier like the sea, he calls them a single species; if they look rather different and he thinks the difference is so great that they would not interbreed even if the opportunity arose, they are classed as two separate species.

With man, we do not have to guess. There is ample evidence that the most different-looking individuals from the most remotely separated parts of the world can interbreed if given the opportunity. Norwegians, Australian aborigines, Bushmen, Malays, and South American Indians are all perfectly capable of interbreeding and producing healthy, completely fertile offspring. The differences among them are at the subspecific rather than at the specific level.

The differences in appearance among men are considerable, however. There is a great variation in size, from the tall peoples of northern Europe and of the upper Nile to the pygmies of the Congo forest. Skin color ranges from shiny black to very pale. Large differences also exist in the texture and distribution of hair on the body, in the shape of the skull, and in the shape of soft parts like nose and lips. No species of wild animal shows anything like this range of variation. The only species with comparable variation are the domesticated ones, dogs, swine, poultry, etc. —which leads some to believe that man is a "self-domesticated" animal.

Human variation is basically geographical: Mongoloid peoples inhabit eastern Asia, Negroid peoples Africa, Caucasoid peoples Europe. The geographical pattern has been greatly disturbed by the large migrations of modern times, especially of Europeans to America, Australia, and South Africa, and of Negroid peoples to America; but it is still apparent (Fig. 4-1). No wild animal is as widely distributed over the earth as man, but

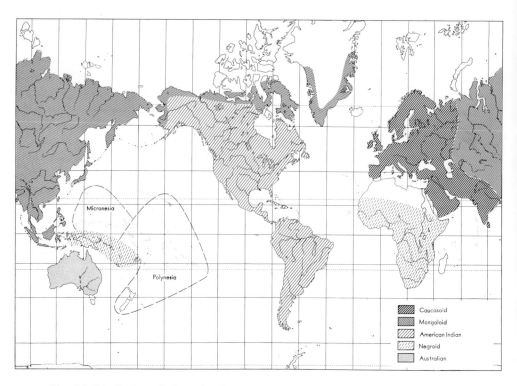

Fig. 4-1. Distribution of the major human racial types before the population movements of modern times.

Legend:
- Caucasoid
- Mongoloid
- American Indian
- Negroid
- Australian

land animals very commonly show geographical variation within their ranges, and there is no reason to suppose that human variation differs in principle from that of other animals.

Sometimes each island of an archipelago will be inhabited by a slightly different variety (or subspecies) of a given species. On a continent, a gradual change in the appearance of a species will sometimes occur as one moves from north to south or east to west; these changes may be more abrupt, so that a series of different populations can be recognized with rather narrow transition zones between them. The first case is said to constitute a *cline,* the second a *Rassenkreis,* or series of subspecies.

This geographical variation is easily understood in terms of genetic theory. Since a new mutation can only spread through the parts of a population that are in contact, when populations are separated by geographical barriers they tend to follow distinct evolutionary histories, and in time they will become so different that even if they did come together again they could not fuse, for they would have evolved into distinct species. When a species inhabits a variety of climates, as on a continent, a mutation favorable in one environment might not be favorable in others, and again result in geographical differentiation.

Many students of evolution believe that geographical variation, resulting from complete or partial isolation of populations, is the chief or even the only way in which a single species population can evolve into two or more species populations. One is led to wonder, then, why man, with so many geographical differences, has remained one species instead of evolving into several.

Modern methods of communication have brought all human populations into contact with each other to some degree, and the sort of isolation that could result in species formation is now clearly impossible. In fact, racial differences are tending to diminish today as large-scale shifts in population increase. It may be that in time geographical variation in human physical appearance will disappear entirely.

It looks as though man's tendency to collect in discrete and separate groups had been counterbalanced, all through his history, by his desire—and ability—to move. As we have seen, a number of distinct hominid types lived in the Old World tropics and subtropics during the early and middle parts of the Pleistocene period. It is difficult, of course, to be sure about the biological relations among these types. But Java man and Peking man, for instance, are so similar that it seems likely that they would be able to interbreed, and thus should be classified together as a single species. On the other hand, it is unlikely that either of these would have been able to hybridize with any of the Australopithecines.

Out of this variety of types only one, *Homo sapiens,* survived. Wherever *sapiens* started—subtropical Africa seems the most likely place—he probably exterminated other hominid types as he encountered them. We can glimpse this process in Europe, where Neanderthal man disappeared rather suddenly, to be replaced by Cro-Magnon man (a true *sapiens*) so that one can presume that the Neanderthal type was exterminated by the newcomers. There may also have been interbreeding—at least some of the skeletons from the caves at Mt. Carmel in Palestine are intermediate between Cro-Magnon and Neanderthal. *Sapiens* certainly spread widely and (in geological perspective) rapidly. He reached North America something like 35,000 years ago, probably by way of the Bering Strait, and in a few thousand years he inhabited both American continents from Alaska to Tierra del Fuego. He must have gotten as far as Australia a very long time ago also, and then remained there in almost complete isolation.

Thus *Homo sapiens,* we can conclude, has been scattered over the earth long enough for the process of subspeciation to start, but the various populations have not been separated long enough, and the separation has not been complete enough, for different biological species to form.

HUMAN RACES

There is no general agreement about the classification of human racial types. At one extreme they are simply lumped into "white," "black," and "yellow" races, and at the other extreme are split up into several dozen recognizable racial types. Coon, Garn, and Birdsell,* in a careful survey of human physical variation, recognize 30 "races," but note that they could just as well have classified man into 50 types. For the purpose of our general discussion, however, we can divide men into a few major racial types: Caucasoid, Negroid, Mongoloid, American Indian, and Australian. Most anthropologists consider the American Indian to be a Mongoloid type, but it is sometimes useful to separate the two. The Australian aborigines might be classified with the Negroid group because of their dark skins, but they are also similar to the Caucasoid group in the texture and distribution of their hair.

CAUCASOID RACES. The Caucasoid, European, or "white" races are characterized by head hair that is generally wavy, and often straight or curly, but is never woolly or frizzy like Negroid hair or as coarse as the Mongoloid. Males usually have a well-developed beard and considerable body hair. The skin varies in color from pale whitish to light brown. The nose is usually narrow and projecting (Fig. 4-2).

One early anthropologist thought the race originated in the Caucasus, and although this idea has long been abandoned, the name has stuck. Caucasoid peoples were distributed very early over Europe, North Africa, the Near East, and into the Indian peninsula. In post-Columbian times, of course, the Europeans have spread all over the world. A wide variety of "subraces" has been distinguished: Mediterranean, Ainu (an isolated group in northern Japan), Celtic, Nordic, Alpine, Armenoid, and so on.

NEGROID RACES. The Negroid races—surely a considerable mixture of rather different types not necessarily related to one another—are characterized by black woolly or kinky hair; by a skin color varying from dark brown to black; by dark brown or black eyes. The nose tends to be broad and flat, the ears small, and the lips thick (Fig. 4-3). Males are apt to have a sparse beard and little body hair.

The Negroid races come from sub-Sahara Africa, from Melanesia, and from scattered parts of tropical Asia. African tribes vary tremendously in physique, from the tall slender peoples of the upper Nile (where the average height is nearly six feet) to the pygmies of the Congo forest. The Congo pygmies average 4 ft. 6 in. in height and resemble other pygmy groups found in the Anadaman Islands, the Malay peninsula, parts of the Philippines, and New Guinea.

MONGOLOID RACES. The head hair is straight, black, and coarse; the skin is yellowish or yellow brown, the eyes brown. The upper eyelid has an "epicanthic fold" that gives the eye a characteristic slit-like appearance. The nose has a low bridge, and the wings of the nostrils are mod-

---

* C. S. Coon, S. M. Garn, and J. B. Birdsell, *Races . . . A Study of the Problems of Race Formation in Man* (Springfield, Ill.: Charles C. Thomas, 1950). Racial characteristics have been reviewed more recently by S. M. Garn in *Human Races* (Springfield, Ill.: Charles C. Thomas, 1961).

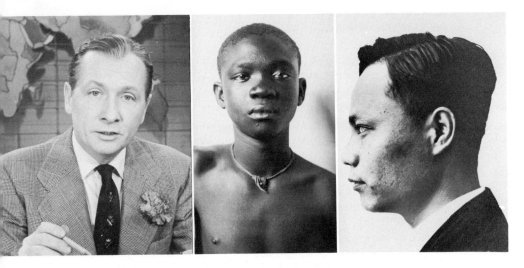

Fig. 4-2. A Caucasoid man. (Courtesy National Broadcasting Company.)

Fig. 4-3. A Negroid man. (Courtesy American Museum of Natural History.)

Fig. 4-4. A Mongoloid man. (Courtesy American Museum of Natural History.)

Fig. 4-5. An American Indian. (Courtesy American Museum of Natural History.)

Fig. 4-6. Australian aborigines. (Courtesy American Museum of Natural History.)

erately spread; the cheek bones are strongly developed, projecting forward and to the side (Fig. 4-4). The incisor teeth often have a characteristic shovel-shaped form. Face and body hair is more sparse than in any other human type.

The "classic" Mongoloid type is found in parts of Siberia, in Mongolia, Tibet, and northern China. The Eskimos are usually classed as a distinct subrace. The Japanese are sometimes classed with Thais, Indo-Chinese, Malays, Burmese, and the like as a "Malay-Mongoloid" group; and the Indonesians may be grouped as another subrace

AMERICAN INDIANS. Since probably many waves of migration swept across the Bering Strait from Asia to America over a long period of time, numerous strains of Old World populations have become blended in the mixture that we call so awkwardly "American Indian." In features, skin, and hair, they are more Mongoloid than anything else, but the epicanthic fold of the eyelid is much less developed, and is completely lacking in the males. The nose and lips, too, are often un-Mongolian (Fig. 4-5). Anthropologists do not agree on the classification of subraces of Indians, although the wide diversity of Indian physique is obvious.

AUSTRALIAN RACES. The head hair is wavy or curly, rarely straight, usually dark or reddish brown in color and often blond in the young. The skin is usually some middle shade of brown. The nose is broad, but prominent rather than flat; the face is rather short, the chin usually receding, the brow-ridges well developed, and the forehead low (Fig. 4-6). Facial and body hair is similar in extent to that of Europeans.

Some anthropologists, on the basis of skull characteristics, have considered the Australians to be the most "primitive" of living humans. Certainly they have been relatively isolated on the Australian continent for a long time, but any attempt to group existing human races into a sequence from "primitive" to "specialized" presents many difficulties. Each race has features that could be called primitive—the hairiness of the Australians and Caucasoids, for instance. By this trait, the Mongoloids would be the most "advanced" of races. One could also take the development of the lips as a criterion and argue that the Negroids are the most human of all. We would be wiser, however, to dismiss such attempts as quite meaningless.

The racial classification we have used here leaves large groups of men unaccounted for. The Polynesians and Micronesians, for instance, are often classified as two separate races, and there has been much speculation about their possible relationship with other races. To the present author they look more like Mediterranean Europeans than anything else and, when well tanned, he can pass as a Micronesian in skin color and physique. But how did these people get to the scattered islands of the Pacific? The most likely explanation is that they moved out from Southeast Asia some two or three thousand years ago, at a time when the population of that part of Asia must have been quite different from what it is at present. Men have been slowly spreading across the planet ever since they became men, and leaving traces of their movements in the odd mixtures of traits found in human populations all over the world. The Australian aborigines have been isolated the longest of any living peoples. Perhaps they can call themselves a "pure" race, but no one else, certainly no European, Asiatic, or African, is in any position to brag about the "purity" of his race. The study of racial characters, their distribution and mixture, remains a fascinating game, and one that may help untangle the complex events of human prehistory.

THE MEANING OF RACE

Considering how much man has been studied, we know remarkably little about him. This becomes evident when we examine the reasons for environmental adaptations among the various human races. Why do the inhabitants of tropical Africa have dark skin and those of Scandinavia light skin? The answer seems obvious: Skin color is an adaptation to climate, especially to sunshine. But the more one looks into the matter, the more complex it becomes. Some students believe that racial traits must be adaptive in origin, must at least be the consequence of some process of natural selection. Others think they may be explained by some non-selective process of random change. The writer is still sitting on the fence, impressed mostly by our ignorance and by the apparently equal plausibility of quite opposite arguments.

Extreme blondness, the sort of skin that continually burns and peels, is certainly a handicap in regions of intense and continued sunshine; extreme blondness is also rare in tropical peoples, although inhabitants of tropical forests are not greatly exposed to sunshine, being sheltered by the dense foliage. There is no evidence, however, that a dark skin is a handicap in Scandinavia. Th color of human skin determines how the skin reacts to ultraviolet radiation—the kind that causes sunburn—but skin color has no effect on the infrared end of the spectrum, the part that is involved in heat transfer. In the infrared region, all human skin, Scandinavian or Negro, acts as a "black body," that is, it is completely absorptive. Human skin, then, of whatever color, does not reflect but absorbs the heat that is radiated to it, and gives off the heat that is brought to the surface from the interior of the body. Careful experiments on men working under conditions of heat stress have revealed no differences in heat absorption between Negroes and blonds.

R. B. Cowles * has suggested that a highly pigmented human skin may be a consequence of natural selection operating under tropical forest conditions. A dark individual is much less visible than a light-colored one;

* "Some Ecological Factors Bearing on the Origin and Evolution of Pigment in the Human Skin," *The American Naturalist,* 93 (1959), 283–293.

since man has undoubtedly been the chief enemy of man for a long time, concealment may have had considerable selective value for hundreds of centuries. We are still left with the question of how man got other skin colors; Cowles himself refuses to speculate.

Adaptive explanations of human racial traits have been most plausibly developed in the book on *Races* by Coon, Garn, and Birdsell, cited earlier. They stress particularly the relation between body build and heat relations: A chunky body is most appropriate for cold conditions and a lanky one for warm conditions. They note that the epicanthic fold of Mongoloids would protect that northern race from the glare of snowfields and that their lack of a beard would give them a selective advantage in extreme cold because of the tendency of ice crystals to form on the hairs.

One trouble with the theory of human racial adaptation to climate is that the advantages of differences in physique are trivial when compared with those of differences in culture. The chunky bodies, slanted eyes, and beardless faces of the Eskimos may be helpful in the Arctic climate, but the Eskimo skill with clothing, shelter, and ways of hunting and fishing is far more important. Eskimos could not survive in their rigorous environment without this cultural equipment; the necessary cultural changes, however, could occur very rapidly in comparison with the long time span required for the action of natural selection on physique.

Hybrids between human racial types are generally intermediate in such traits as skin color, hair distribution, and facial features, indicating that these characteristics are each controlled by a number of different genes. David Bonner and Stanley E. Mills have discussed the genetics of skin color in a chapter on "Genes and Man" in the book on *Heredity* in the present series. They also include some discussion of the genetics of the various blood group systems that have been found in man. The study of these has contributed considerably to our understanding of races because, through the study of blood serum, it is possible to compare the frequencies of particular genes in different human populations.

RACE AND CULTURE

Race and culture act as independent variables—that is, the fact that a particular human racial type is associated with a particular kind of culture is a consequence of history rather than of biology. Our culture—the civilization developed in Western Europe by Caucasoid peoples—has dominated the world for nearly 500 years, and we are apt to think that "Westernized" and "civilized" mean the same thing. The Chinese emperors of the past had quite different ideas, as apparently do the present rulers of that great country. Highly complex cultures—civilizations—have been developed more or less independently by Mongoloid peoples in China, Caucasoid peoples in India and the Near East, Negroid peoples in various parts of Africa, and American Indians in Central America and

Peru. Techniques and ideas diffuse from race to race, culture to culture. The fact that our particular race and civilization has been dominant for a few hundred years is no guarantee that it will remain so forever.

Conflict between cultures is an ancient phenomenon, with a far more impressive history than race conflict. The Greek distinction between Hellenes and barbarians was a cultural, not a racial, distinction; and a mistrust of foreigners, of outsiders, of people who act differently (whether they look different or not) is an almost continuous theme in human history, while racial conflict is rare and sporadic—perhaps because the different races had little contact with one another until modern times.

Both racial and cultural conflicts are subjects for study by social scientists. There may be some ultimate biological basis, related to the basis of conflict behavior sometimes seen in other animals, like the vocal fighting over territory of the howler monkeys. But this is so deeply buried under history, economics, and learned behavior that digging for it at the present time is hopeless. From the broken bones and fractured skulls of fossil hominids, it seems clear that men have been cruel to each other for a very long time, and nothing is more important for our future safety and happiness than to find the causes of these attitudes and to develop ways of dealing with them. To say they must always be with us because they always have been is nonsense: Where would we be if we took this attitude toward infectious disease?

There is no clear evidence for racial differences in intelligence. Individuals obviously vary greatly in ability; this variation has both biological and social origins, and it is usually very difficult to untangle the two. We now realize that the argument over "nature and nurture," over the relative importance of heredity and environment, is futile. Both are important. Every individual is born with a certain heredity, a certain potential; how this potential finds expression depends on circumstances of development, on environment, on culture, on education. Individuals with comparable genetic potentialities will act differently as adults, depending on whether they were raised in Chinese, Hopi, Bantu, French, or American cultures. But individuals in the same culture, exposed to similar environmental influences, will also show differences that are rooted in their genetic potential. If we ever develop detailed explanations of individual human behavior, they will probably result from the studies of both geneticists and psychologists. Unfortunately, at the present time these two kinds of scientist have very little acquaintance with each other's work.

But let us turn from human variety to human numbers. The study of population, of reproduction and mortality, in our species clearly involves both biological and social factors, and in this case there has been a great deal of interchange between the two fields of science.

Human
Populations

CHAPTER FIVE

Man, in all his varieties, is the most abundant species of mammal on the planet. We cannot be sure exactly how many people there are, because the inhabitants of many parts of Africa, Asia, and South America have never been carefully counted, but a generally accepted estimate for 1960 is 2.9 billion people, scattered in uneven densities over the six populated continents (Fig. 5-1).

Rats and mice, too, are extremely numerous—many billions of rodents live on the North American continent alone —but there are over 300 species of rodents in the United States and just one species of man. The only species comparable in abundance with the human animal are small ones such as codfish, sardines, and houseflies. If we look not at numbers of individuals but at total bulk of protoplasm, man might well win out over all other animals. And the number of men is shooting upward at a fantastic rate.

Approximately 187 babies are born every minute, or about 270,000 every day. Something like 142,000 people die each day, leaving a surplus of 128,000, which is equivalent to the population of a fair-sized city. The total population of the

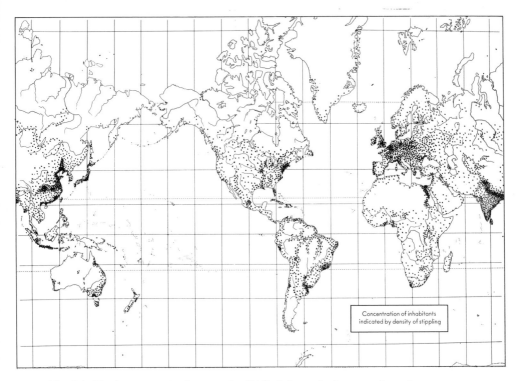

Fig. 5-1. The human species is unevenly distributed, mostly because of varying climates and resources, partly as a result of historical developments.

world is thus increasing by about 47 million every year; in effect, we gain a new Chicago every month, and however admirable Chicago may be, a new one every month should give us pause.

The human population is now rising at a rate of about 1.7 per cent per year. If people keep multiplying at this rate, the world will be packed with about 25 millions of millions in some 600 years, or one person for every six square yards of land surface. Manhattan Island is considered overcrowded today, and it has nearly 35 square yards of land surface for every inhabitant. The idea that the Sahara may become several times as crowded as present Manhattan is dizzying. It is, in fact, unthinkable; the present growth rate must be abnormal and temporary.

Analyzing trends in human population growth and predicting future developments are the province of a special branch of the social sciences, demography. Human behavior, whether of individuals or groups, is clearly governed by many factors that cannot readily be understood in terms of biological principles. Biology, however, is much concerned with the dynamics of population growth and equilibrium among organisms in general, and although it in itself cannot explain the special case of man, biological principles are certainly involved. Because of a close relationship between biological and social approaches to population study, demography has formed an important bridge between the two fields of science.

49

The word "population" means "peopling"—the numbers of people inhabiting a place, a region, or the world. The concept of numbers, of counting, is inherent in the idea, and population study is closely bound up with statistics. (Statistics, it is interesting to note, originally referred to affairs of the state, the enumeration of resources or of people.) The word "population" has long been extended to include all sorts of organisms besides people, so that one can refer to populations of mice or fish or insects or plants; but the word always implies numbers and statistical methods of analysis. Since statistical methods are also used in the study of inanimate objects, economists sometimes refer to populations of automobiles or bolts or other products of manufacture.

An inclusive definition of "population" thus must be broad, something like "an aggregate of similar items conforming to a particular definition in time and space." The term essentially serves to isolate a limited category of living beings or of objects for special study: people in the United States, schoolchildren in Michigan, Mohammedans in India, or deer in England. The definition usually must include the kind of item, and the limits of geography and time. Changes in the population, then, depend on birth (natality), death (mortality), and movement in or out of the geographical limits (migration).

Reproduction

Demographers distinguish between the concepts of *fertility* and *fecundity*. Fecundity refers to the capacity of the individual or the population to reproduce, fertility to the actual reproductive performance. Fecundity is the reproductive potential, a more or less theoretical concept that is useful chiefly in making comparisons among different species. The fecundity of a species depends on physiological factors—on the length of time required to reach sexual maturity, on egg and sperm production, on conditions surrounding fertilization, on rate of embryonic growth, and the like. Fertility depends more on ecological factors—it is the expression of the reproductive potential in a particular environment.

The fecundity of the human species has presumably been constant for a very long time, but fertility varies greatly in different populations, and in a particular population at different times. The fertility of a population—its actual reproductive performance—is most often expressed in terms of the *crude birth rate*. This is the number of live births per year per thousand of population. The usefulness of this figure for comparison or prediction is limited because populations vary in such things as the proportion of females of reproductive age, in the proportion of married females, and so on. Demographers consequently prefer to apply more sensitive measures, such as *age-specific birth rates, net reproductive rates,* and *stand-*

ardized birth rates, but since these require the sort of detailed and accurate statistics that are not available for large parts of the world, the crude birth rate remains the most common and easily used figure for comparisons among human populations.

Maximal human reproductive rates are difficult to establish because the populations that presumably have the highest rates also have the poorest statistics. The highest known rates are in the neighborhood of 50 births per year per thousand population, and rates of this magnitude generally characterize populations living at subsistence agricultural levels.

In Europe and North America, birth rates have decreased greatly during the last hundred years. In the United States, for instance, the birth rate in 1900 was 38 per year per thousand (or 38 0/00 in demographers' shorthand), reached a low of 16.6 0/00 in the depression year of 1933, and remained around 17 0/00 until 1940 when an increase started that persisted through the war and postwar years. In France the decline started earlier than in other countries, being 28 0/00 in 1840 and falling to 15 0/00 by 1940. All Western countries have shown similar drops in birth rates, though the decline has been later and slower in countries like Italy, Spain, and Portugal. In general there is an inverse relation between birth rate and economic development, degree of industrialization, and educational level of the population. Great differences in birth rates among different social, economic, and educational groups also exist even within a given country, and rural families tend to be larger than urban families.

The differences in birth rates are clearly the consequence of social rather than biological factors; they stem from differences in such things as age at marriage, marriage rates, contraceptive practices, and so on. Social customs that result in birth limitation have been common in many human societies. Taboos of one sort or another on sexual intercourse have often been in force, particularly the widespread bar against intercourse with a nursing mother; various contraceptive methods also appear to be ancient and widely known. But perhaps the most important fertility controls until modern times were abortion and infanticide, which were practiced not only by many primitive societies but also by some of the ancient civilizations.

Mortality

The earth's human population at the present time is growing rapidly, yet in many parts of the world the birth rate is declining. The growth, then, must result from the fact that the death rate is declining even faster than the birth rate.

Mortality is usually expressed in terms of the *crude death rate,* which is the number of deaths per year per thousand population. It, like the crude birth rate, is only a rough measure, since it does not take into account such factors as the age composition of the population, and demographers prefer to use more precise measures when they can. Statistics for much of the world, however, are incomplete and unreliable, and this is most true of the regions with the highest death rates.

The lowest death rates in the world are now maintained in the Western countries. The rates reported in 1959, for instance, were 5.9 0/00 for Israel, 7.1 0/00 for the Netherlands, 8.9 0/00 for Norway and Australia, 9.1 0/00 for New Zealand, 9.4 0/00 for the United States, 11.3 0/00 for France, and 11.7 0/00 for the United Kingdom. The differences among these countries are due not so much to varying health conditions as to differences in the age composition of the populations—the French population having the highest proportion of old people, the Israeli the lowest—which illustrates the deficiency of the crude death rate as a measure of mortality conditions. Very few countries currently report death rates above 20 0/00, but this is undoubtedly because the deaths in many countries are inadequately reported. Experts of the United Nations estimate that the death rate for much of the world in the mid-twentieth century is probably between 22 and 25 0/00.

The difficulty of getting accurate statistics increases as one goes back in time, but there is no doubt that the decline in the death rate is a modern phenomenon. In 1800 the death rate was about 33 0/00 in Sweden and 25 0/00 in France, and the rates in these countries have shown a steady decline from decade to decade. In modern times the control of specific diseases has clearly been the most important factor in lowering death rates. In the United States in 1900, for instance, the crude death rate was 17.2 0/00, with tuberculosis as the leading killer, followed by pneumonia and infant diarrhea. In 1950 the death rate was 9.6 0/00, with heart disease as the leading cause, followed by cancer, cerebral hemorrhage, and accidents. The infectious diseases have become relatively less dangerous and their place has been taken by the infirmities characteristic of old age.

Biologists often distinguish between "ecological death"and "physiological death." When death results from environmental factors, from pathogenic organisms, from physical accident, from lack of food and the like, it can be called ecological. But if an organism is protected from such environmental hazards, death still comes as a consequence of some breakdown in the organization of the individual. We start to die as soon as we are born. The rate of growth tapers off and then ceases when adult size has been reached, and this is followed by a gradual impairment of faculties—loss of muscular tone, a slowing of reactions, and various physical signs of aging like the graying of hair. In the human female, reproductive ability ceases with menopause; in the male, the loss of reproductive potential is less sharply marked. The machine of the body, working less and less efficiently, finally ceases to function. Sometimes it is impossible to say which part of the machine has caused the final breakdown, and we have death from "old age," physiological death.

The greatest effect of modern medicine has been on ecological death.

Infant mortality has been cut in a spectacular way. Students of medical history believe that in the seventeenth and eighteenth centuries about half of the babies born in European cities died in infancy, and this has remained true in many parts of the world right up to modern times. On the other hand, medicine has made little progress with the degenerative diseases of old age; life expectancy at birth is very different in the Western world now from what it was 50 years ago, but for people who have reached the age of 70 or 80 years, the expectation of continued life has not changed much. Very few people at any time have lived more than 100 years. In a survey of over 800,000 life insurance cases in Great Britain, where accurate records could be presumed, there were only 22 instances of people living beyond 100 years.

With animals in nature, almost all deaths are ecological deaths. One never comes across a senile rabbit or even a senile fox. Ecological death has also been the rule with man over most of his history, and in much of the world death with man is still primarily ecological, resulting from infections, food deficiencies, and other hazards of the environment. With modern medicine and sanitation, however, it is possible to shift this pattern drastically and quickly through intelligent action. In Ceylon, for instance, an intensive program of malaria control was started in 1946, chiefly through a spraying campaign with DDT to destroy the mosquito carriers of the disease. Within two years, the crude death rate dropped from 20–22 0/00 to 13–14 0/00; not only was malaria brought under control, but the death rate from infant diarrhea was greatly reduced, apparently because houseflies as well as mosquitos were killed by the spray campaign. The birth rate remained the same, with a consequent sudden increase in the rate of population growth for the country.

No one questions the importance of controlling disease and suffering wherever and whenever possible, but since we can now regulate the death rate to some extent through social measures we are faced with the question of whether comparable attention should be given to means for shifting the birth rate, especially in countries where a population is already living at a subsistence level. How is economic development to be fostered in the face of constantly growing numbers? This is a problem for economics and other social sciences, but it also has biological implications. It is interesting, then, to look at what we know about the history of population growth.

POPULATION HISTORY

As difficult as it is to get precise figures about the numbers of people living at the present time, in view of the fact that careful censuses have not been made in many parts of the world, it is vastly more difficult as we move back in history. Many clues still can aid us, however, and the reconstruction of past conditions from them can become a fascinating study.

Man presumably was not a very abundant animal during the Stone Age. He required an estimated two square miles of good hunting territory to support himself, and since there are only about 20 million square miles of such land on the earth, the maximum possible human population during the long period of the Paleolithic must have been something like 10 million. Although artifacts such as flint tools are sometimes surprisingly common and give the impression of an abundant population, it seems more likely that these represent accumulations from relatively few people over very long periods of time. Man in the Paleolithic was an integral part of the biological community; he was just one of the predatory animals in the community, and his numbers were strictly limited by the abundance and availability of his prey.

With the shift from food-collecting to food-producing, which took place during the so-called Neolithic Revolution, all of this changed. When man started clearing land and planting crops, when he started altering the nature of his relations with the biological community, his numerical relations also changed. A great many more people could be supported on a square mile of land than before, and ample archaeological evidence indicates that man did, during the Neolithic period starting some 10,000 years ago, become more numerous.

As man developed methods of storing and transporting food, large aggregations of people became possible, and his villages became cities. Scholars estimate that the population of the Roman Empire, at the time of Augustus, was about 55 million, with 23 million living in the European provinces—but this was a peak, not reached again for a thousand years.

The American sociologist Kingsley Davis * has made a special study of the history of population on the Indian subcontinent. He concluded that the population at the time of Chandragupta, in 300 B.C., was between 100 and 140 million. Since he estimated that the population in the year 1600 was 125 million, it appears that the population of this great region changed very little during the 2,000-year interim. Rapid population growth did not start in India until about 1850, but in the next 100 years it more than trebled, reaching 433 million (India and Pakistan combined) in 1950, with no limit in sight.

The British economist, Sir Alexander Carr-Saunders, has made estimates for the growth of world population in modern times that are generally accepted by demographers. His figures are graphed in Fig. 5-2.

World population probably changed very little during the tens of thousands of years of the Paleolithic; a considerable increase undoubtedly accompanied the invention of food-producing; the development of cities and empires some 5,000 years later was likely marked by another major increase; and a further spurt occurred in modern times with the Industrial

* For bibliographic references on population history, see M. Bates, *The Prevalence of People* (New York: Scribner's, 1955).

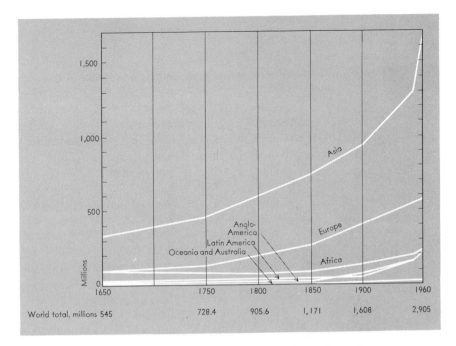

Fig. 5-2. The increase in the population of the world and of the continents from 1650 to 1960.

Revolution. Although the effects of this growth are primarily the concern of the social sciences, they also involve biology in many ways, particularly through the influence of the ideas of Thomas Robert Malthus.

MALTHUS AND DARWIN

Modern population study began with a little book published anonymously in 1798 entitled *An Essay on the Principle of Population as It Affects the Future Improvement of Mankind.* The book immediately stirred up controversy and criticism which led the author to dig up more facts and to publish, in 1803, a much larger and more carefully documented second edition without the pretense of anonymity. Four more editions were prepared before Malthus died in 1834, but the changes in later editions were mostly matters of detail.

The eighteenth century was a period of great optimism about the future of mankind: Science and reason seemed to open up infinite possibilities to French philosophers such as Rousseau and Condorcet. With the aid of reason and science, they believed, man could live not only much longer but much more happily. Malthus' father was a friend and disciple of Rousseau, and the ideas in the *Essay on Population* arose out of discussions, stimulated by French philosophical thinking, between Thomas Robert and his father about the perfectibility of man. Malthus *fils,* looking about him, could see little evidence that man was tending toward perfection; in fact, it seemed to him that the attainment of perfection was

55

blocked by the inexorable laws of nature. He proposed two basic postulates:

First, that food is necessary to the existence of man.

Secondly, that the passion between the sexes is necessary, and will remain nearly in its present form.

The consequence of the passion between the sexes is the multiplication of people, and the more people there are the more offspring they are able to produce. Population thus tends to multiply in geometric ratio: 1, 2, 4, 8, 16, 32, and so on, rapidly, up to astronomical numbers. Malthus calculated that, unchecked, population would double every 25 years. Resources, however, show no such inherent ability to multiply. By improving agriculture, by putting new land under cultivation, man could possibly add to his resources, but only in an arithmetic progression: 1, 2, 3, 4, 5. The result is a constant pressure of population on resources, on the means of subsistence, which in turn produces starvation, disease, war, all the vices and miseries of mankind. Given these natural laws, how could mankind attain perfection?

In the 1803 edition of the *Essay,* Malthus revised the wording of his "dismal theorem," stating it in the form of three propositions:

1. Population is necessarily limited by the means of subsistence.
2. Population invariably increases where the means of subsistence increase unless prevented by some very powerful and obvious checks.
3. These checks, and the checks which repress the superior power of population and keep its effects on a level with the means of subsistence, are all resolvable into moral restraint, vice, and misery.

It is possible, then, to escape from inevitable vice and misery through "moral restraint," by which Malthus meant restraint from marriage and procreation until means were available for the support of offspring. Malthus nowhere considers the question of birth control, though his name is often associated with birth-control movements. The debate over the ideas of Malthus has continued through the years, with many important consequences in economic and social thought. In biology, the Malthusian propositions have a historic importance because they led directly to the development of the theory of natural selection by Charles Darwin and Alfred Russel Wallace. Darwin notes in his *Autobiography:*

In October 1838, that is, fifteen months after I had begun my systematic enquiry (into the mutability of species), I happened to read for amusement "Malthus on Population," and being well prepared to appreciate the struggle for existence which everywhere goes on from long-continued observation of the habits of animals and plants, it at once struck me that under these circumstances favourable variations would tend to be preserved, and unfavourable ones to be destroyed. The result of this would be the formation of new species. Here then I had at last got a theory by which to work. . . .

Years later Wallace, in the East Indies, read the same book, thought of the same theory, wrote it down at once, and sent it to Darwin for criticism. The result was the famous Darwin-Wallace papers read before the Linnean Society on the evening of July 1, 1858, from which stem the present notions we have about the mechanisms of biological evolution.

Malthus wrote in terms of populations and their means of subsistence. Today in biology we use a different vocabulary to discuss the same ideas. The possible reproductive rate of any particular kind of organism is called its "biotic potential." This potential is never fully realized for any animal or plant; parasites, predators, accidents, and failure of food supply intervene to cause the premature death of many individuals. These causes of death are summed up in the concept of "environmental resistance."

The environmental resistance turns out to be much more complicated than anything Malthus imagined, and in the balance of nature the population of most organisms is checked long before the ultimate limit of the food supply, of the means of subsistence, is reached. The study of this situation, of the limiting factors on population growth, is one of the main preoccupations of modern ecology.

With man, the Malthusian propositions sometimes seem to hold. The population of Europe in Malthus' day and that of India a hundred years later consumed all the available food and was under the constant danger of famine if the food supply was lessened by unfavorable events. The disastrous potato blight that swept Ireland in 1845 left a famine in its wake that was a classical demonstration of Malthus' "dismal theorem." Modern Western man, at least, has apparently escaped the Malthusian trap by enormously increasing the productivity of land through scientific developments. Whether this escape is only temporary is a matter for debate among the experts. People in the more advanced countries today certainly lead a safer and more pleasant existence in an economy of abundance cushioned by a margin of safety in the goods available for sustenance. One of the great problems of our time is learning how to spread this abundance to all people; much of the world only too obviously still lives at a subsistence level, with the Malthusian propositions an ever-present threat.

"Environmental resistance" has a rather different meaning for man than for any other organism, because he has developed so many aids for survival —and, for the few, comfort. In the biological realm, he has domesticated animals and plants, invented ever more advanced agricultural techniques, fought disease with increasing effectiveness, and managed his resources more and more efficiently. These topics we shall examine in the following chapters.

Domestication

CHAPTER SIX

The present numbers of people on the planet could not be supported were it not for the few kinds of other organisms that man has brought under domestication or cultivation. The large and complex societies that we call civilizations depend, even more narrowly, on a small group of cereals, especially wheat, rice, and corn (maize). These cereals give a high yield of food per acre, and they are easily stored and transported, qualities which make possible the development of cities and the freeing of a large proportion of the population from direct food-producing activities. The tubers (potato, taro, manihot) give an equally high food yield, but they are more difficult to store and transport and, probably because of this, have never served as a basis for city formation. The Mayan and Incan civilizations of America had few domesticated animals, and these were unimportant either as food or as sources of power, which shows that large-scale animal domestication is not a necessary prerequisite for the development of complex societies.

It is convenient to class the cultivated plants and domesticated animals together as *cultigens*. The relationship between

58

man and the cultigens can be looked at as a form of symbiosis, of close mutual interdependence of two species of organisms. It is a unique form of symbiosis in that it has developed in the relatively short span of a few thousand years through cultural modification of man and biological modification of the cultigens. Man has not changed biologically: hunting man and gardening man are the same animal. There is no "gardening instinct," no inborn tendency to go out and gather seeds and plant them; agriculture has to be learned, and the learning is transmitted from generation to generation. The cultigens, on the other hand, have become for the most part biologically very different from their wild ancestors. Corn is an obvious example; it could no longer survive without man to husk the ears and plant the kernels.

Many parallels exist between human activities and those of the social insects, and this is also true of cultivation, where we can find an analogy with the fungus-growing ants of the New World tropics and termites of the Old World tropics. The ants of the genus *Atta* will serve as an example. They are major agricultural pests in many parts of tropical America because they snip bits of leaves from many kinds of plants (including cultivated species) and carry them to their nests. The leaves are not eaten, but are used as a substrate in special chambers of the nests for the growing of a particular species of fungus, which does form the food of the ants. When new queen ants swarm from old nests on their nuptial flights, they carry fragments of the fungus in cheek pouches from which fungus gardens are established in the new nests. A special caste of tiny workers, the *minims,* forms the agricultural labor force, whose job it is to weed out unwanted growths and maintain the gardens.

The ants are completely dependent on the fungus for their food supply. The fungus species cultivated by the ants are unknown except in association with ant nests, indicating that the fungus is also completely dependent on the ants. The interdependence of the ants and fungus is thus a classic case of mutualistic symbiosis.

We have every reason to suppose that the relationship between ants and the fungi they cultivate is geologically ancient. Ants from Oligocene amber, dating back some 40 million years, are hardly distinguishable from living species, and it is logical to suppose, if their appearance is so similar, that their habits were also similar. The fungus relationship is a product of biological evolution, and each generation of the cultivating organism takes it up, instinctively. Man has been cultivating plants for perhaps ten thousand years, and his behavior in cultivating is entirely learned—which makes the similarity purely analogous, however striking.

How did this peculiar human behavior get started? All we can do is speculate, on the basis of such facts as we can gather. But before doing this it may be useful to take a brief look at the different kinds of relationship that man has established with other organisms.

Fig. 6-1. Man as predator. (New York Public Library Picture Collection.)

If we go back and try to imagine the place of *Australopithecus* or *Pithecanthropus* in the biological community, we see him primarily as a predator. The protohominid or early hominid niche in the community was comparable with that of the social canines, such as the wolf. Man probably became a relatively effective predator quite early, because he successfully adopted tool-using and developed a cohesive social organization. He probably was never exclusively a predator, but ate fruits, nuts, and tubers as supplementary foods. At times, the tables would be turned, and men would be prey for other predators such as lions and crocodiles, although his group habits must have given him a large measure of protection. His tribal or family groups, however, would not protect him from parasitism, and some of the human parasites, especially the intestinal helminths, the malarial *Plasmodia,* and body lice, show evidence of having evolved right along with man.

Early man, then, was predator, prey, and host for parasites, and also a sort of general scrounger or collector of oddments like fruits, nuts, and insect grubs. It is clear from cave drawings, for instance, that he quite early learned to rob bees' nests of honey. There seems to be no general ecological word for this miscellaneous collecting activity of an organism, so let's call it "collecting."

With the development of tool-making and using, man's collecting activities extended greatly. We have a record of his making of stone tools, and to some degree of his use of bones, but he must at the same time have used wood in many ways, and learned the special properties of many kinds of plants. If one can judge from contemporary food-gathering tribes, Stone Age man must have acquired an extraordinarily detailed knowledge of the possible utility of the animals and plants among which he lived— as sources of food, fiber, medicine, poison, and paint. By the time of the later Australopithecines, man had undoubtedly entered into a far wider variety of relations with other members of the biotic community than any other animal ever has.

These relationships multiplied as man learned to interfere more drastically with the biotic community. One of the first things he must have done was to build shelters. We talk about "cave men" and man may have been primarily a cave animal in a few situations, during glacial times in Europe, for instance, but mostly we associate him with caves because they are most readily preserved and found. Men living in the open have probably always far outnumbered the cave dwellers. And the men in the open surely learned to construct shelters—even chimpanzees make nests.

If you build even a crude sort of shelter in wild country, a wide variety of animals will promptly move in on you to share the shelter—scorpions, cockroaches, lizards, mice. There is a special word for the organisms that live in ant and termite nests without doing any particular damage or giving any particular benefit. They are called *inquilines*. It may be useful to extend this word to man's uninvited guests and call them human inquilines. The house mouse, the brown rat, the Norway rat, and the roof rat belong in this category, as well as numerous kinds of insects (Fig. 6-2).

Fig. 6-2. Baby mice—among the inquilines of human habitations. (Courtesy American Museum of Natural History.)

As soon as man starts making very extensive systems of shelters, a new process is involved—the clearing of land. In clearing, man creates what we may call an "open habitat," which is a rare situation in nature. The special open habitat is immediately invaded by a series of plants, with their associated animals, that are uncommon or unknown in the usual stable and closed biological community. These are the plants we call weeds. Man today has converted so much of the land surface into an open habitat that we forget how unusual this condition is in the absence of man. Weeds seem to us common and tough, but in the parts of the world that man has not yet greatly disturbed, like the northern coniferous forest or the rain forest of the upper Amazon, these "common" plants disappear, or become extremely scarce. They are found on sandbars in the rivers, or in spots where some giant of the forest has fallen—that is, in the few open habitats that are not man-made, and, of course, always around the little clearings that men make even in these remote places.

Weeds, then, are really "opportunists." Although this word could equally well be applied to the inquilines, it is convenient to make a distinction between the organisms that move into human shelters and the organisms that find a sudden opportunity because of man's interference with the previously existing community structure. The one relationship is much more intimate than the other. Mice are inquilines, but pokeweed and robins are opportunists.

We come now to the cultigens, the animals and plants that man deliberately propagates and encourages: a late development, but now the most important of man's biological relationships. Perhaps we should make a distinction between cultigens and pets. Many primitive peoples keep tamed animals around their settlements. Such animals are not maintained from generation to generation, but are captured individually from the wild. Our current idea of a pet, of course, is an animal kept for amusement or because of affection. Biologically it would be more useful to distinguish between pets and cultigens on the basis of whether or not they have been modified through their association with man. By this criterion, dogs would be cultigens, while cacti grown in a rock garden would be, like macaws, pets. Some organisms are now in transition from "pets" to "cultigens." The Australian budgerigars, or "love birds," that breed so readily in captivity are one example. But while this may be the origin of such cultigens as common flowers, it hardly explains important crops or animals.

Man's relationships with fauna and flora can thus be separated into at least eight categories of organisms: his prey, his predators, his parasites, his objects of collection, the inquilines, the opportunists, the cultigens, and the pets. These relationships are here classified biologically; a classification in cultural terms would be quite different, involving magic and totem, food, medicine, ornament, and the like. Our present interest, however, is to examine man's relationship with the cultigens.

We do not know how man first discovered the value of domesticating animals and cultivating plants; perhaps we never shall with any certainty, since our evidence must always be indirect. But we can weigh the relative plausibility of different theories, and in the process gain in our understanding of the nature of man and of the evolution of his culture. Since modern man's relations with the rest of the natural world depend so largely on this man-cultigen relationship, speculation as to how it came about is certainly a legitimate preoccupation of science.

The dog is generally considered to be the oldest of the domesticates. (It seems odd to call the dog a "cultigen," although if we are to be consistent about our vocabulary, that is what he is.) When and where the dog was first domesticated, how this came about, and what wild species was involved are all still matters of controversy. But such questions, curiously, are matters of controversy in the case of most of our important cultigens. It is always surprising to stop and realize that man has not domesticated any important animal or plant within historic times, despite his vaunted knowledge and science; we still depend on the cultigens that were brought under control in the dim twilight of prehistory. Minor exceptions to this are such laboratory animals as fruit flies (*Drosophila*) and hamsters, some of the microbes such as the mold that produces penicillin, and a few other things like rubber and quinine trees.

One cannot help but wonder why this is so. Perhaps prehistoric man had so thoroughly ransacked the living world that all possibly useful cultigens were discovered. Perhaps after cultivation was well established, man became too removed from the natural world to bother with trying to tame more things. Within historic times, however, there has been a vast exchange of cultigens among peoples in different parts of the world, so that there has been a steady enrichment of the resources of any particular culture. This exchange, or diffusion, process makes in itself a fascinating subject for study.

The post-Columbian interchange of crops between the Old and New Worlds makes a good case history. Both biological and cultural factors must be considered in explaining cultigen distribution; soil and climate must be favorable, but there must also be cultural acceptance. The spread of potatoes and corn (maize) in the Old World can only be explained in terms of both kinds of factors. The failure of breadfruit, a staple starch of Oceania, to be valued as food in the West Indies is perhaps purely a cultural one.

The diffusion of cultigens can thus be more accurately traced than their origins, but let us for a moment look at this problem of origins. To get back to the dog, students of the subject hold three different theories: that the domesticated dog originated from a canine species now extinct, that it is descended from one of the existing wild species, or that it represents a mixture of several wild species. The domesticated dog can hybridize with many kinds of wild canines in different parts of the world—in North America, for instance, with both the timber wolf and the coyote, which do not hybridize with each other. There are undoubtedly, then, elements from different wild canines in many of the modern breeds of dogs. Carl Sauer has argued plausibly that the first domesticated canine may have been a species native to Southeast Asia that is now extinct.* This may have been an animal something like the Australian dingo. We have, however, no certain evidence for this extinct species.

But how did the first dog, whatever it was like, get started on the road to domestication? One theory is that the dog adopted man, took to hanging around, jackal-like, to feed on the offal left from kills made by men, and that a closer and closer association gradually grew up between the two kinds of animals. Man and dog complement each other, since the dog has a much keener sense of smell and hearing, and man better sight and better ability at solving problems. Certainly they can learn to hunt together more efficiently than either can hunt alone. One difficulty with this theory is that specialized hunting breeds of dog appear to be a rather late development, and there is no evidence that the great hunting cultures of the Old Stone Age had any dogs at all.

Another theory is that the dog started as a pet. The writer has seen South American Indians catch the rare tropical American "bush dog" *(Icticyon)* when very young and keep it as a pet. Early cultures may well have had these same pet-making habits, with the ancestral dogs proving to be particularly docile and able to breed under captive conditions. The order in which animals were domesticated after the dog is not known.

Sauer, in his book on agricultural origins, has discussed the conditions that are necessary for domestication, for the transition from food-collecting to food-producing. He thinks that the beginnings of agriculture probably took place among people already settled and living in an economy of abundance. "The saying that necessity is the mother of invention," he remarks, "largely is not true. The needy and miserable societies are not inventive, for they lack the leisure for reflection, experimentation, and discussion." A suitably fortunate condition, he feels, would most likely occur in a fishing culture near rich fresh waters in a mild climate. An environment with a great diversity of plants and animals would be favorable, since it would provide a variety of materials for experimentation. Plant cultivation probably started in woodland rather than grassland, because primitive agriculturists even now find it impossible to deal with grass, but relatively easy to girdle or cut the trees of woodland.

It is overwhelmingly probable that agriculture was developed at least

* Carl O. Sauer, *Agricultural Origins and Dispersals* (New York: American Geographical Society, 1952).

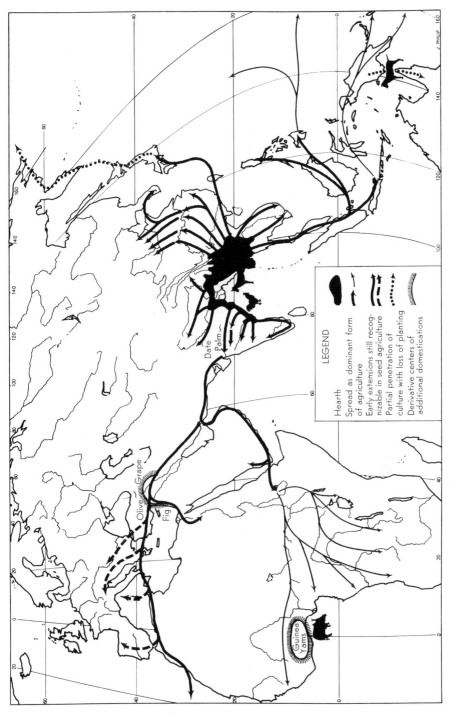

Fig. 6-3. Old World planting and household animals. (Sauer, Agricultural Origins and Dispersals, Amer. Geog. Soc. Bowman Memorial Lectures, 1952, Ser. 2, Pl. I.)

twice completely independently, in the Old World and in the New. Perhaps there were three independent centers, Southeast Asia, Southwest Asia, and the American tropics; and agriculture possibly developed, without outside hints, in several other places and at different times (Fig. 6-3).

Our earliest certain knowledge of cultivated plants and domesticated animals is from the Near East, from sites like Jarmo in Iraq, which date from about 5000 B.C. (Fig. 6-4). The people of Jarmo had barley, two kinds of wheat, the domesticated goat, and possibly other animals, such as sheep, cattle, pigs, and horses.* This surely, however, does not represent

* Robert J. Braidwood has given a general account of the findings at Jarmo in his book, *Prehistoric Men* (Chicago: Chicago Natural History Museum, 1957).

Fig. 6-4. Artifacts excavated from Jarmo, a Neolithic village site in Iraq. (From Robert J. Braidwood, Prehistoric Men. **Chicago: Chicago Natural History Museum, 1957.)**

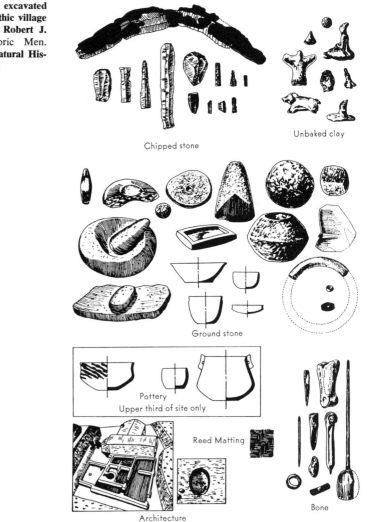

Unbaked clay

Chipped stone

Ground stone

Pottery
Upper third of site only

Reed Matting

Architecture

Bone

the beginning of agriculture. Sauer thinks that the first cultivation and domestication probably took place in Southeast Asia, which seems to be the original home of such household animals as pig, fowl, duck, goose, and perhaps dog, and of such important tropical cultigens as bananas, taro, and yams. Since these plants are all propagated vegetatively, by tubers or cuttings, they were likely among the first cultivated, for it is easier to put a piece of a tuber or stem back in the ground after the plant has been dug up than it is to learn to plant seeds.

Southwest Asia appears to be the home of an entirely different set of cultigens: of cereals such as wheat, oats, and barley, and of the grazing mammals. Native to tropical America are corn, several vegetatively propagated sources of starch (cassava and potatoes to name two), and a variety of vegetables and fruits. Fiber plants were also important among the early cultigens in both hemispheres. The Americans, curiously, domesticated relatively few animals—the llama, the alpaca, the guinea pig, and several others.

THE MODIFICATION OF CULTIGENS

The most anciently cultivated plants and domesticated animals have been modified considerably in the course of their association with man. A great many of them have become completely dependent on man and are unable

Fig. 6-5. (A) Breadfruit, (B) cassava, (C) yam.

to live and propagate without his help. We can call these the "obligate cultigens," in contrast to the "facultative cultigens" that can still, under some circumstances, get along by themselves. This division is analogous to that between the obligate and facultative pathogens of infectious disease.

Corn (maize) is an extreme example of an obligate cultigen. The plant is completely helpless without man to husk the ears, separate the seeds, and plant them. It cannot reproduce by itself even in a completely "open" habitat with no competition from other plants. Since the densely populated civilizations of the Andes and Middle America could not have developed and maintained themselves without this cereal, we could easily regard the man-corn relation, in tropical America at least, as a case of mutualistic symbiosis. But the relation differs from symbiotic relationships such as that of the leaf-cutting ant and its fungus in that only the cultigen is biologically modified. Civilized man, food-producing man, is, as far as we can tell, biologically identical with food-collecting man, but the biological nature of cultigens has altered markedly. How has this come about?

Corn, wheat, cotton, and their wild relatives have been subjected to particularly intensive genetic studies, made in part at least with the object of trying to reconstruct the biological histories of the cultigens.* In general, the rigors of natural selection have been relaxed under man's care. Mutations that would have no survival value in nature could persist and spread within populations, and might be favored because of some fancy of the human caretaker. The genetic variability of cultivated populations would thus tend automatically to increase. There is also clear evidence of hybridization, accidental or purposeful, between cultigens and related wild species, further increasing the diversity of the gene pool (Fig. 6-6).

We are now faced with the crucial question of what role man has played in guiding the evolution of his cultigens. Both Darwin and Wallace depended greatly on the analogy with artificial selection in developing their theory of natural selection, and we can see very clearly how effective the process has been in developing new breeds and in changing old ones in modern times (Fig. 7-3). But it is difficult to assess the effectiveness of selection in the early stages of agriculture. Contemporary primitive peoples often seem to exercise a sort of negative selection by eating more desirable materials and using less desirable ones for reproduction. Yet if this had been the general Neolithic custom, it is difficult to see how the cultigens would have developed as they did.

Mangelsdorf discovered a particularly beautiful documentation for corn in the stratified refuse accumulated over a period of three thousand years in the rock shelter known as Bat Cave in New Mexico. The shelled cobs from this refuse show a slow but steady increase in size over this period, and loose kernels also gradually enlarged and changed in character during

* See "The Mystery of Corn" by Paul Mangelsdorf in *Scientific American,* July, 1950; and "Wheat" by the same author in the July, 1953, issue.

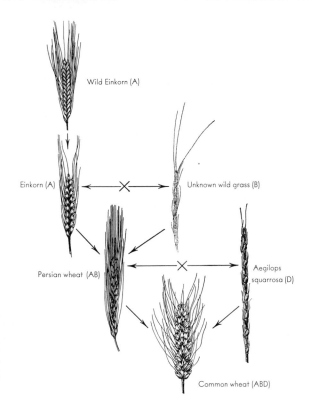

Wild Einkorn (A)

Einkorn (A) ←—×—→ Unknown wild grass (B)

Persian wheat (AB) ←—×—→ Aegilops squarrosa (D)

Common wheat (ABD)

Fig. 6-6. Evolution of common wheat. Wild einkorn (7 chromosomes, A) evolved into einkorn, which, crossed with a wild grass (B), gave rise to Persian wheat (14 chromosomes, AB). When this wheat was crossed with another grass (D), common wheat (21 chromosomes, ABD) resulted. (From Paul Mangelsdorf, "Wheat," Scientific American, **July 1953. Reprinted with permission. Copyright © 1953 by Scientific American, Inc. All rights reserved.)**

the long time span. The original wild corn was probably a pop corn, a grass with small hard seeds each enclosed in a glume and born on the tassle, seeds that exploded when exposed to heat. Geneticists have been able to produce such a grass experimentally from modern corn although it is unknown in the wild and may be extinct. One can imagine how early man might have accidentally discovered the food value of these popped kernels and thus been led to bring the plant into cultivation. Once cultivated, the whole complicated sequence of genetic events leading to modern corn becomes explicable; the slow changes in the nature of the plant were then accompanied by changes in the methods of using it.

Interestingly enough, there is evidence that the ancestral wheats were first eaten as parched grains and then as gruel, with the baking of bread coming later. Changes in the biological nature of the plants and in the cultural ways of using them came along slowly after cultivation had started. Such shifts in methods of use may have been common, and part of our difficulty in imagining the beginnings of the cultigens stems from our ignorance of long-lost customs. In the case of domesticated animals, their first significance may have been magical or religious rather than utilitarian.

But whatever the beginnings, man and his cultigens are now united in a firm and mutually dependent partnership. The partnership is maintained by the process we call agriculture, and we shall look at the biological implications of this in the next chapter.

Agricultural
Biology

Man's agricultural activities are, in essence, an effort on his part to rearrange and simplify the food relations that usually prevail in the biological community. To understand this, let us look first at the biological community without man. From the point of view of food behavior, we can class organisms as producers, consumers, and decomposers. The producers are the plants that, through photosynthesis, are able to build up complex organic compounds from carbon dioxide and water and thus provide the material to sustain all other members of the community. The consumers are the animals: the herbivores that live directly off the plants and the carnivores that live off other animals. The decomposers, mostly bacteria and fungi, play the final role by reducing the complex materials of living stuff again to simple constituents.

Any such statement as this is an oversimplification, but it will serve our present purposes. Relations among the consumers are particularly varied, but we can roughly distinguish the first-order consumers that live directly off vegetation, the second-order ones that live off the first-order members, and so on. We end up, by this system, with the conventional "food-chain," such as the one that goes from grass to hawks: grass—grass-hoppers—frogs—snakes—hawks. Nothing in nature, of course, is this simple; when you start to trace who eats whom in the community, you end, not with neat chain-like sequences, but with a complex network, a "food-web" rather than a "food-chain."

Within this web, however, we can detect certain patterns. The first-order consumers tend to be small and numerous, the second-order, larger and fewer, and so on. On this principle, the "pyramid of numbers" can be built up (Fig. 7-1). The energy transfer within this system has been measured, and a great loss in energy has been found to occur in each step away from the basic producers. Approximately 6 per cent of the energy available at any one level is passed on to the next, and thus the number of possible steps away from the producers is strictly limited: Five is about the maximum possible number of "trophic levels." * Actually, a very large proportion of the living stuff never travels through the animal parts of the cycle at all; many plants grow, die, and decay, with their constituent materials going directly into new plants.

Man is an animal, one of the consumers. Without fire, man must have been primarily a second- or third-order consumer, living mostly on grazing animals, insects, fish, and the like; he could act as a first-order consumer only when eating fruits, nuts, and a few other such special plant products. When he learned to use fire for processing vegetable materials, he was able to become a first-order consumer, but he still was not able to use very many kinds of vegetable material, for oak leaves, pine needles, and tree trunks do not make nutritious human food no matter how well they are cooked. The obvious answer (however slowly and painfully arrived at in prehistory) was to replace inedible vegetation with edible kinds, to substitute plants not directly useful to man with those that are.

With the development of agriculture, then, man was able to move into the efficient position of being a first-order consumer, living on rice, wheat, corn, potatoes, cassava, taro, and so on. Many human cultures became primarily vegetarian, though a taste for meat generally persisted. As a carnivore, man used agriculture to become a relatively efficient second-order consumer by growing grass for grazing animals like cattle and sheep, and corn or other grain for animals like hogs and poultry.

In the food webs of the natural community, many different kinds of organisms often share the same food supply. In the process of developing agriculture, man has not only shortened food chains, but has tried to eliminate this competitive aspect of the community. He does not want to share his cabbages and corn with insects, or his poultry with hawks, or his sheep with wolves. He has tried, with increasing success, to remove all these complicating by-ways in the natural web.

* For a discussion of this, see G. E. Hutchinson, "Homage to Santa Rosalia or Why Are There So Many Kinds of Animals," *American Naturalist,* 93 (1959), 145–159.

Fig. 7-1. A "pyramid of numbers." Man catches large fish, which feed on more numerous smaller fish, which in turn feed on multitudinous first-order consumers, which live on the green plants at the base of the pyramid.

Man, therefore, has tended to substitute ecological simplicity for complexity. This has resulted in a great gain in efficiency, which in turn has enabled man to become very numerous and to develop his present fantastic rate of reproduction. One wonders, in the face of this, why the natural community has tended to be so complicated.

Ecologists are coming to feel that the consequence of diversity is stability.

There is accumulating evidence both from field observations and from laboratory experiments that the more complex the community, the more stable it is, both in terms of the system as a whole and in terms of the fluctuations in the numbers of its individual members. It would be out of place to examine this theory in any detail here, but it is easy to visualize in terms of an analogy. Just as the stability of a national economy is promoted by diversification, so is the stability of a biological community. A simple system may be destroyed or upset by a shift in any of its parts, while the diversified system includes many possibilities for compensation or substitution. Of such is the "balance of nature."

A man-controlled community is more subject to disaster than a diversified natural community. Where man depends on a single crop, destruction of that crop by drought or plague becomes a threat that must be continually guarded against. A landscape of wheat can be harvested efficiently by man, but it also represents a paradise for wheat-loving insects and fungi which can build up catastrophic populations if not checked in time. One of the problems of agriculture, therefore, is the need to balance efficiency against safety.

THE MAN-MADE COMMUNITY

Since the Neolithic Revolution, since the shift from food-collecting to food-producing, man has gradually lessened his dependence on particular biological communities and at the same time increased his ability to replace the "natural" communities with systems that fit his needs, or his whims. Over a very large part of the earth's surface, man has become the ecological dominant; much of the landscape can only be understood in terms of human actions, which is only too obvious in the patchwork of fields and highways and towns seen from the air in the eastern United States or Europe or China. Forested areas sometimes look "natural" enough, but these, too, are dominated by man in the sense that they are left there because he wants or needs them, and in the more tailored countries the forests are planted and groomed. To be sure, one can fly across the upper Amazon or over the Congo or the northern woods of Canada and not be greatly impressed by the effects of man. But such areas are being increasingly encroached upon and surely they, too, will one day be under human control. Man, in short, has become a geological force, molding the terrestrial landscape.

Man acts not only by replacing vegetation, but also by changing water relations through irrigation and drainage, and perhaps presently he will be making rain. His engineering works are impressive. We think first of the canyons of Manhattan and of the great dams of the world, but the rice terraces of the Philippines and the dikes of the Netherlands represent equally drastic physical alterations of the landscape. The amount of space covered by cement becomes rapidly larger. Someone has estimated that the area now covered by highway and railway right-of-ways in the United States is equivalent to the area of the state of Georgia.

The ordinary biological community is a self-maintaining aggregation of interdependent organisms. One community is rarely sharply separated from the next, but the communities are nevertheless roughly recognizable as a series of more or less independent systems of energy transfer. The forest is made up of numerous kinds of organisms ultimately dependent on the trees; the lake of organisms dependent on the plant plankton; the savannah of organisms dependent on the grass, and so on.

This geographical localization of the transfer of energy and materials has ceased with modern man. It started to break down in ancient times with the first growth of trade and was accelerated by the widespread transportation and storage systems developed to supply food in the classical empires of Greece and Rome. With the transportation revolution of the nineteenth century, the breakdown became complete, at least within the area of Western civilization. There is no necessary relation now between the food eaten in any town in the United States and its geographical location. Southerners may eat more rice and grits, northerners more potatoes, westerners more steaks, and people on the Eastern Seaboard more oysters, but these are cultural preferences rather than necessary consequences of geography.

In any American town, food and beverages are drawn from almost the entire world: bananas from Honduras, coffee from Brazil, sugar from Cuba, spices from the Orient, vegetable oils from Africa, olives and wine perhaps from California, but also perhaps from southern Europe. The possibilities are somewhat limited by the attempts of many national states to be self-sufficient through the imposition of tariff barriers on imports. Despite these nationalistic tendencies, however, the trend toward a global human community is quite clear and, barring catastrophe, apparently inevitable. Man's mind and activity are becoming a unifying and dominant force on the planet.

Various efforts have been made to coin a word or phrase to denote this characteristic of our time; some have suggested calling it the "psychozoic era" or "anthropozoic era." Vernadsky's word "noösphere" (from the Greek, noös, mind) has perhaps gained the widest acceptance as an expression of the way in which the age-old relationships within the biosphere are being altered by the activities of the human mind.* The noösphere is still far from being equivalent to the biosphere, but the gap, on land at least, is closing rapidly.

Man has found it necessary to alter many of the chemical cycles of the ordinary biological community by supplying such materials as nitrates and

* Pierre Teilhard de Chardin has discussed this concept in "The Antiquity and World Expansion of Human Culture" in W. L. Thomas, Jr., ed., *Man's Role in Changing the Face of the Earth* (Chicago: University of Chicago Press, 1956).

phosphates in "artificial fertilizers." He has developed an extensive system of interregional transportation of such chemicals, and he has learned how to manufacture nitrates, though he depends on mining for the phosphates. Some people deplore this as unnatural and unhealthy and there is a widespread cult of "organic gardening." Certainly civilized man has often been wasteful of plant and animal products that might be restored to the soil, and this has many dangers. But man started to be "unnatural" a long time ago and there is no way back—though this is no argument for being indifferent to the dangers.

To maintain the simplified food chains of the man-made community, man must wage constant "warfare" against competitors for crops, especially insects and fungi. Increasingly we have come to depend on chemical poisons—on insecticides and fungicides—as weapons in this struggle. This, too, has its dangers and a great deal of thought has gone into the development of "biological" methods of control: the breeding of plant strains resistant to insect or fungus attack, the cultivation of parasites of pests, the use of crop rotation or of planting methods unfavorable to the pests. But let's look at the problems of pest control in more detail.

PEST CONTROL

The majority of the hundreds of thousands of species of insects live directly off the leaves, stems, roots, or fruits of seed plants. The British oak, *Quercus robur,* has some 225 species of insects that feed on it primarily, and a large number of other insect species that feed on it occasionally. Oaks, to be sure, are particularly "favored" by insects, but every kind of seed plant has a few species of insects that eat it. In the undisturbed biological community, however, the plants seem to get along all right, despite the hordes of insects they support. The insects are kept from reaching damaging numbers by the checks and balances of nature—parasites, predators, diseases, dispersal problems.

The situation in the usual garden plot of a primitive culture is not greatly different from that in the biological community. All sorts of cultigens are grown together in apparent disorder in the gardens of American Indians, Pacific Islanders, and African tribesmen. Plenty of insects infest the garden, but usually not in sufficient numbers to cause disastrous damage. But this situation changes tremendously under conditions of intensive agriculture.

One reason for this, of course, is that "civilized" man is intolerant of any competition for the products of his cultigen. A worm in an apple may not eat much of the apple, but modern man simply doesn't want *any* worms in his apples; his less "advanced" cousins in other cultures, on the other hand, might not care about the worms one way or the other. Extensive cultivation, however, does cause a real enough increase in the insect threat. This is partly because large areas planted to a single kind of crop provide unusually favorable circumstances for the multiplication of the pests of that crop—the host then does not need to be searched out from among a wide variety of other plants—and partly because man, in moving materials around the globe, has also accidentally moved a great many insects. An insect pest, in a new country, escapes the parasites and predators that normally keep it in check, so that it is free to multiply to the limit of the food supply. In one study of 183 insects considered to be major crop pests in the United States, 81, or 44 per cent, were found to be clearly of foreign origin, and others were likely so. We can probably safely generalize that about half the major insect pests of any area have been accidentally brought into that region from somewhere else.

When an exotic insect becomes established in a new country and reaches pest proportions, an intensive search is usually touched off for parasites and predators in its homeland that could be imported as a means of biological control. This sort of practice has been particularly successful in places like the Hawaiian Islands, where both crops and pests are foreign to the native biota; the further importation of pests of the pests thus helps restore the balance. For the most part, however, the various attempts at biological control have not met the needs or wishes of the agriculturists, and they have come to depend chiefly on chemical control.

Chemical control is not entirely unknown in nature. The various plant alkaloids and other poisons (nicotine, for example) were developed, according to one theory, primarily as a means of protecting the plant against insect attack. If this explanation is correct, the system has not been notably successful: tobacco plants and other alkaloid-producing members of that plant family are subject to attack by many kinds of insects, although concentrated nicotine has also long been successfully used as an insecticide. The whole antigen-antibody system in animals can also be viewed as a "natural" form of chemical control.

Yet man's adoption of chemical control measures against his competitors can be considered as a new and "artificial" process, only remotely analogous with things like antibiosis (the word we now use for chemical antagonisms between organisms—first observed with the mold *Penicillium* and bacteria). New methods of chemical control have been developed rapidly in recent years, and many people believe we have not been properly alert to the possible dangers of these methods. Controversy has centered particularly around DDT and related substances. DDT (dichlorodiphenyltrichlorethane) was synthesized long ago by the Swiss, but its insecticidal properties attracted little attention until the Second World War when both the Germans and the Allies discovered its value as a delousing agent. Since then, this chemical has found its way into every aspect of insect control.

DDT is toxic not only to insects but to men and a variety of other animals; susceptibility varies with the species and with the individual. It is an extremely persistent chemical—a wall painted with a dilute solution may be lethal for months to mosquitoes that land on it. It is also a cumulative poison, so that very small amounts, harmless in themselves, may build up to a threshold of obvious damage. The evaluation of the possible dangers of DDT is thus a slow process, and new effects are constantly being discovered. An intensive campaign of spraying elms with DDT, for instance, can produce a surprisingly detrimental reaction in the local bird populations: apparently the poisoned elm leaves drop to the ground, are eaten by earth worms, and when robins subsequently eat the worms, they are poisoned. Many unexpected and sometimes disastrous consequences have also resulted from the use of DDT in ponds and marshes for mosquito control: Fish and marsh birds may be killed incidentally.*

Man's prime interest is in man, and more and more people are worrying about the possible effect of these cumulative poisons on the human population. The danger is now recognized in the case of milk, and DDT and similar chemicals are prohibited in barns where milk cows are kept; milk with any trace of these chemicals is also barred from interstate commerce. Since the insecticides also affect many other food products, concern has been aroused about the possible extent of the danger to health.

Chemical control of insects and other pests is clearly desirable in many sorts of situations: It is often the only practical method of pest control. But biologists insist that we should pay a great deal more attention to other, less artificial, ways of manipulating the environment; they maintain we should know a great deal more than we do about the ecology of control measures, so we can understand what we are doing and be prepared for the possible adverse consequences.

NATIVE AND FOREIGNER

As Alfred Russell Wallace long ago pointed out, a geographical pattern exists in the distribution of land organisms on our planet (Fig. 7-2). He recognized six major realms: the Neotropical (South and Central America and the West Indies), the Nearctic (North America down through the highlands of Mexico), the Palaearctic (Europe and northern Asia, from Britain to Japan), the Oriental (India, Malaya, the Philippines, and adjacent regions), the Ethiopian (Africa south of the Sahara), Australian (Australia and New Guinea and the islands east of Borneo and Java). New Zealand forms a special case, as do the oceanic islands such as those of the Hawaiian archipelago. These major regions have been separated by climatic and geographical barriers through much of geological history. Land connections have appeared and disappeared in such places as the Isthmus of Panama and the Bering Straits, and climates have sometimes shifted greatly, but the basic pattern has persisted for a very long time. Modern man, with his elaborate and diverse transportation systems, has now established connections among all these regions, purposefully and

* Rachel Carson has given a detailed and persuasive account of the dangers of insecticides in her book, *Silent Spring* (Boston: Houghton Mifflin, 1962).

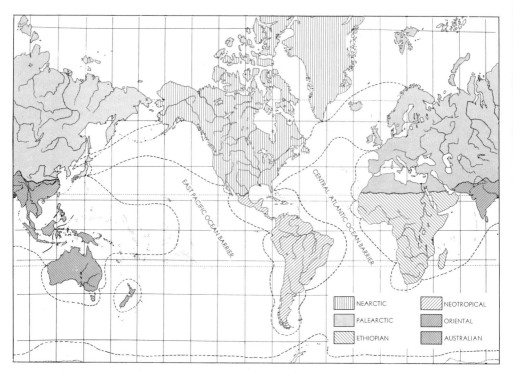

	NEARCTIC		NEOTROPICAL
	PALEARCTIC		ORIENTAL
	ETHIOPIAN		AUSTRALIAN

Fig. 7-2. Modern man has purposefully or accidentally transportated many animals and plants across the barriers separating Wallace's faunal regions.

accidentally transporting organisms all over the world, with many different consequences.*

In general, of course, organisms move most easily between areas of similar climate: between the Mediterranean and California, between Europe and Australia or New Zealand, between tropical America and tropical Asia and Africa. We cannot say, however, that we really understand the factors that govern the establishment or failure of a species introduced into a new region. Several attempts were made to bring starlings into North America before their successful introduction in 1890 and 1891; many early attempts to establish rabbits in Australia failed.

Man's total impact as an agent in the transplantation of organisms has been enormous. The United States Office of Plant Introduction, for instance, has brought something like 200,000 named species and varieties of plants from all over the world into the United States to test the possibilities of their use and establishment. Most of these, of course, were never grown outside of experimental gardens, but it still represents a major operation in the alteration of plant distribution.

Meaningful statistics on the numbers of insects and other organisms accidentally carried by man from one part of the world to another are

* For a lucid discussion of this phenomenon, see Charles Elton, *The Ecology of Invasions by Animals and Plants* (New York: Wiley, 1958).

difficult to come by. The U.S. Public Health Service reports that 80,716 airplanes were inspected by quarantine officials in the 10-year period between 1937 and 1947, and that insects or other arthropods were found in 28,852 of the aircraft. As we have seen, probably half the major insect pests of most regions are foreign species, accidentally introduced. In continental areas, the native fauna is so large and complex that there is little room for foreigners, and only occasional immigrants are able to establish themselves. Oceanic islands, like the Hawaiian archipelago, represent a quite different situation; the native fauna is apt to be small and highly characteristic, limited to species that have become established through rare accident over long stretches of geological time. Such places are easily open to invasion, and almost half the insects now in Hawaii have been accidentally (or sometimes purposefully) imported during modern times.

Man has frequently regretted the consequences of his introductions. The starlings now have few friends in the United States, and the rabbits in Australia none. The Indian mongoose, introduced into Hawaii and some of the West Indies in the hope that it would control rats in the cane fields, turned out to be a predator on harmless native birds and reptiles, and had little effect on the rats. On the other hand, of course, man in most parts of the world has come to depend on introduced cultigens for his basic food, and many of the less important introductions, for reasons of sentiment or sport, have had only happy consequences.

The moral here is that we should think carefully about what we are doing before undertaking mass transportation of organisms; and, again, we need to learn a great deal more about the ecology of any given situation. The animals and plants that have been accidentally or purposefully introduced into various parts of the world in the past offer many opportunities for study that have hardly been utilized. They can, in a way, be considered as gigantic, though unplanned, experiments in ecology, geography, and evolution, and surely we can learn much from them.

CROP IMPROVEMENT

We should not discuss the subject of "agricultural biology" without mentioning the great progress that has been made in recent years through the application of genetics to plant and animal breeding. "Hybrid corn" (Fig. 7-3) is of course the spectacular case, but every major crop has been affected to some degree by work in genetics. Although our primitive ancestors accomplished incredible feats in domesticating and modifying organisms without benefit of modern science, the application of scientific methods to agricultural problems has revolutionized man's resource relations in the last hundred years or so, and the future possibilities seem unlimited.

The present writer, however, feels that every effort should be made to keep close relations between theoretical and practical knowledge, that in

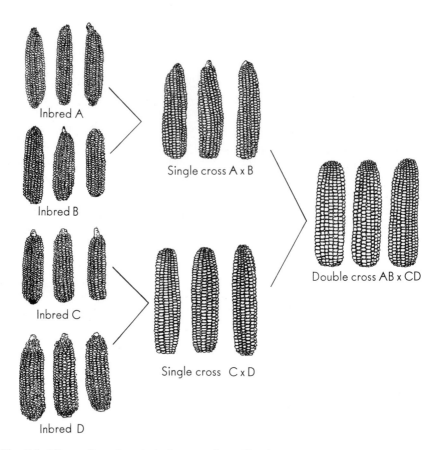

Fig. 7-3. After earlier attempts to improve the uniformity and productiveness of corn through breeding had failed, researchers in 1920 succeeded in producing an effective hybrid corn. First, superior inbred strains were isolated, reducing their vigor and productiveness but increasing their uniformity. Next, the inbred strains were crossed by pairs (A B, C D, etc.) to produce single crosses, which were much more productive than the inbred strains but were too expensive for general use. Finally, two single crosses were crossed to produce double-crossed seed, which are less uniform than single crosses but almost equally productive, and inexpensive enough for widespread commercial use.

some ways agricultural biology, especially in the United States, has tended to become too widely separated from its supporting sciences. Ecology and agriculture, particularly, have tended to move apart, though both are fundamentally concerned with the interrelationships between organisms and the environments in which they live.

FISHERIES

Man is a land animal, and it is thus not surprising that he has made more progress in modifying biological communities for his purposes on land than in the sea or in inland waters. Man, however, has also been culturally amphibious for a very long time, and artifacts such as fishhooks testify to his ancient exploitation of aquatic resources. As was suggested in the last chapter, fisheries, either coastal or more likely inland, may have provided the opportunity for the transition from a roving to a settled life.

But man's biological relations with the sea have changed little since the beginning of the Neolithic. During the time that man has been busily engaged in remaking the landscape, shortening food chains, upsetting biological communities, shifting from gathering to producing, he has remained essentially a gatherer of marine products. Fishhooks, nets, traps, and harpoons have undergone no drastic modification within historic times. We have learned to use different materials—substituting steel for bone, for instance—and to make very different kinds of boats, but we cannot point to any "revolution."

There are exceptions, of course. The oyster industry virtually "cultivates" the oysters. Fish ponds, anciently maintained in the East, are becoming increasingly common in Western regions, and "fertilization" techniques designed to maintain dense populations of edible fish species are being adopted. Although fish hatcheries are commonly used for stocking lakes and streams, the fish are mostly for sporting purposes.

The waters of the world, both salt and fresh, remain very important food resources for man. Fish are the main source of protein for many large human populations. Investment in fisheries research is increasing in many parts of the world, but the expenditure is minute when compared with the research effort on land resources. Perhaps we shall never be able to control the seas as we control the lands—which may be fortunate, both for marine organisms and for us. In the overcrowded future, the seas may be the only wilderness, the only escape from ourselves, that remains. We can, however, pollute easily enough, and we have managed major destruction in the vicinity of our great port cities.

The problems of pollution, however, are most easily dealt with as one aspect of man's relations with the resources of the planet, one aspect of conservation or resource management. Before considering this, let's look at man's ways of dealing with his own parasites, at the biological and ecological elements in health and disease.

Health
and Disease

CHAPTER EIGHT

In the complex web of food relationships within the biological community, animals not only eat, but in turn are eaten. Agricultural biology is primarily concerned with man eating; medicine and public health with man being eaten. The tendency in the evolution of agriculture is to simplify food chains and eliminate organisms that compete with man for food; the tendency in medicine is to make man terminal in the food system, in other words, to eliminate organisms that eat him.

If we ignore decomposers and scavengers—organisms that live off dead bodies, excretory products, or waste materials— we can concentrate on predators and parasites. Predators and parasites are easy enough to distinguish in ordinary usage: A predator is a big animal that kills and eats smaller ones, while a parasite is a little organism that lives off bigger ones. The lion is a predator of sheep; liver flukes and fleas are parasites on the same sheep. As soon as we start a sophisticated analysis of food relationships among animals, however, the distinction becomes less pronounced, although the words are convenient for our purposes.

If we define a predator as an animal that directly kills and eats another animal, the prey, then man has long ceased to be prey. People are still occasionally killed and eaten by lions, crocodiles, and sharks, but for the vast majority of mankind this is, and long has been, a very remote possibility. Tools and social organization have made the human species, for all practical purposes, immune to predation.

Parasitism is another matter. Man has been able to cope with the big things easily, but the little things that feed on him have continued to flourish. The parasites are a primary cause of disease.

Disease and health are polar words: That is, like hot and cold, they have meaning only in relation to each other. Disease is ordinarily defined as "a departure from a state of health"; contrarily, health is "the absence of disease." To give hot and cold more precise meaning, we devise a scale of changes with reference to particular events, such as the freezing and boiling of water. The many efforts to establish a comparable sort of a scale for measuring "degrees" of health have all failed. One suggestion is that the zero, the absolute lower limit, of health is death, that as long as there is some life, there is some degree of health. With such a scale, the upper limit, the maximum level, of health would be the perfect functioning of the organism in all respects, but no satisfactory criterion for this maximum has ever been formulated.

Although it is difficult to give disease a precise, scientific definition, we all know what it means and use the word easily enough in our daily conversation. Man was able to recognize disease states in ancient times and must have tried even then to do something about them. Every primitive people has some way of trying to cope with disease, and at the dawn of history, in Egypt and Babylonia, we find the beginning of an elaborate medical lore. The roots of modern biology are deeply entangled with the history of medicine, and biology and medicine remain closely related today. It may be interesting, then, to glance very briefly at the history of ideas about disease.

THEORIES OF DISEASE

A widespread belief persists among primitive (and sometimes not-so-primitive) peoples that disease results from the possession of the body by a spirit or a god. The logical way to cure the disease is thus to get the spirit to depart, either by enticement or by threat, and this becomes the job of the witch-doctor. His treatment, oddly enough, often worked. In the still little-understood body-mind relationship in disease situations, the confidence of the patient in his doctor is sometimes more important than precise medication, and the witch-doctor above all had the confidence of his patients.

Primitive man, even with the mumbo-jumbo of sorcery, acquired a considerable body of empirical knowledge. Pharmacologists are gaining increasing respect for this folk medicine and spend large sums searching for and testing native remedies from various parts of the world. We were alerted to the value of tranquilizers, which are so widely employed today in the treatment of mental illness, by our modern discovery of the ancient Hindu practice of using extracts of the plant *Rauwolfia* as a therapeutic agent. Ancient man, of course, in his intimate contact with nature had vast stretches of time in which to find the properties of natural substances, but his knowledge of drugs, poisons, and foods still seems extraordinary.

To get a glimpse of the prescientific approach to knowledge, let us examine the history of aspirin, which was discovered in modern times. Here is the description by Rene Dubos: *

Consider, for example, the history of aspirin—that least celebrated and most useful of all remedies. Having noted that rheumatic pains were most frequent among people living in low wet areas, the Rev. Edward Stone postulated that God in His mercy had certainly placed in these same areas some antidote for the pains. Inspired by this faith, he discovered in 1763 that an extract of the willow bark was indeed highly effective in relieving pains of rheumatism. Within half a century chemists had established that the willow extract owed its therapeutic efficacy to a substance which they called salicylic acid, from the Latin name of the willow, *salix*. Salicylic acid was synthesized by Gerland in 1835 and its derivative, acetyl salicylic acid, by Gerhardt in 1853. The latter substance was marketed under the name aspirin and for reasons still unknown proved even more useful than salicylic acid itself.

With the beginning of civilization and systematized thought, men grew dissatisfied with the simple idea that evil spirits cause disease. The suspicion that disease is a consequence of some upset in the balance of natural forces occurred to many people. This notion gradually crystalized in Western civilization into the theory of the four humors, which started with the Hippocratic writings, was developed by Galen and the Arabs, and dominated European medicine all through the Middle Ages (Fig. 8-1). Health, this theory said, results from a proper balance between blood, phlegm, yellow bile, and black bile; each humor had its own characteristic—hot or cold, moist or dry—and when equilibrium among them was destroyed and disease set in, health could be restored only by restoring the equilibrium. The theory evolved into a highly sophisticated system of medicine, which was often effective; and traces of it remain in our vocabulary today in the words *sanguine, phlegmatic, choleric,* and *melancholic,* all adjectives describing temperament.

The contagious nature of many diseases was recognized by ancient man, but the idea of *infection,* of disease being produced by the invasion of the body by foreign organisms, usually microbes, dates from the middle of the nineteenth century, when Louis Pasteur (1822–1895) began his dramatic experiments that attracted such wide attention. Pasteur's ideas did not

* Rene Dubos, *Mirage of Health* (New York: Harper, 1959), p. 129.

develop in a vacuum, and a careful history of medicine would give credit to many contemporaries and predecessors, but Pasteur rightly remains the hero of the theory that infection causes disease, just as Darwin, living at the same time, remains the hero of the theory of evolution.

Pasteur's work triggered an intense hunt for the microbes lurking behind every disease, and by the end of the century most of the major human pathogens (except for the viruses) had been discovered. The theory of infection as the cause of disease triumphed over all the other theories, and the clear success of sterilization and aseptic techniques in surgery instilled in people a fear of "germs" that still persists. Pasteur's work had the incidental effect of giving all microbes a bad name, though the economy of nature could hardly function without them.

We now realize that infection is only part of the disease story. The role of fresh foods in curing scurvy was long known, but this was not explained until the present century with the discovery of vitamins, and a whole category of "deficiency diseases" was uncovered. Perplexing problems of resistance, susceptibility, and immunity to disease were disclosed, showing that even in infections the disease situation depends on complicated interactions of host, pathogen, and environment, about which we still have much to learn. The work of Sigmund Freud opened the lid into the mysterious world of psychosomatic illness. We began to find out about allergies and about diseases rooted in

Fig. 8-1. The four temperaments that reflect the four medieval humors, as depicted in a late fourteenth-century illustrated manuscript. (A) Sanguine fellow: loves mirth and music, wine and women. (B) Phlegmatic type: given much to rest and sloth. (C) Choleric chap: all violent, fierce, and full of fire. (D) Melancholy man: a heavy look, a spirit little daring. (Bettmann Archive.)

genetic, hereditary sources. With the control of infections, the "degenerative diseases" of old age came into the center of the stage. Cancer took its place as the most important of medical problems—but remained elusive.

We have now no "single cause" for disease; it is difficult even to classify diseases, because infections, hereditary dispositions, nutrition, psychological stress, and social environment often blend, in bewilderingly subtle ways, to produce any given diease. Any elementary discussion of disease, then, is bound to oversimplify and perhaps be misleading. With this warning, we can examine a particular category of diseases, the infections, which are of special biological interest.

MAN AS HOST

In discussing disease, we immediately encounter vocabulary problems, partly because the various biological and medical sciences dealing with diseases have often developed independent histories and separate vocabularies. An *infectious disease* is a disease caused by the entrance, growth, and multiplication of a foreign organism within the body. A *contagion* is thus one kind of an *infection,* a kind in which the infecting organism goes directly from one host to another. A contagious disease is "catching"— measles, for example—but many infections, such as yellow fever and malaria, cannot normally pass directly from one human host to another, but must travel via intermediate hosts, in these cases particular species of mosquitoes, which are called the *vectors* of the disease.

The organism causing a disease is called a *pathogen* (from the Greek *pathos,* suffering, and *gens,* bearing). The pathogen of the medical vocabulary is roughly equivalent to the parasite of the biological vocabulary, although all parasites are not pathogenic. An organism may live entirely at the expense of another organism without causing obvious damage or clinical symptoms of disease, and is thus not pathogenic. This sort of situation blends imperceptibly with those in which both kinds actually benefit from the association to those in which neither organism can live without the other. The range therefore, is from parasitism to mutualistic symbiosis.

The human pathogens include a considerable variety of organisms. The most important kinds are viruses, bacteria, fungi, protozoa, and helminths.

VIRUSES.   Virus in Latin means slime or poison (as of snakes) and has a long history in English as a general word for infectious or poisonous material. It gained its specific meaning as the name of a class of living materials, the *filtrable viruses,* during the present century. In the search for methods of sterilization toward the end of the nineteenth century, it was found that materials passed through fine porcelain filters could be freed of all particles, including bacteria. Then, in 1892, a young Russian, Dimitrii Iwanowski, noticed that liquid from tobacco plants with mosaic disease retained the ability to infect new plants after it had been "sterilized" by filtering, but he attached no importance to this at the time. Six years later, a Dutch botanist, Beijerink, making the same kind of experiments, came to the conclusion that the infectious agent in tobacco mosaic disease *must* be living and yet fluid—a "contagious living fluid" he called it. At about the same time, the infectious agent of the foot-and-mouth disease of cattle was found to have similar properties, and the special science of virology thus had its inconspicuous beginning.

Viruses are defined as obligate pathogens that are so small they pass through the fine porcelain filters that exclude the smallest bacteria. A very great deal has been learned about them in the days since Iwanowski and Beijerink, but we are still arguing about their true "nature," particularly about whether they represent a really primitive form of life or have evolved from bacteria and represent an extreme of specialization for a parasitic way of life. They are "obligate pathogens" because no one has yet found them in the absence of disease conditions, and none have ever been grown in a medium free of living cells. Once a virus has been isolated, the virus particles can be photographed and studied with the electron microscope, but if there are "free-living viruses" in sea water or in the slime of ponds, we have no way of finding them, since we can recognize viruses only by the symptoms of the diseases they cause.

Viruses are now known to cause many human diseases: smallpox, influenza, measles, polio, rabies, mumps, yellow fever, and a whole class of diseases grouped as "encephalitides." They are involved in the little-understood "common cold." They have been found associated with numerous pathological conditions in all sorts of animals and plants, and the viruses that infect bacteria, the bacteriophages, have been subjects of particularly intensive and rewarding study. Many bacteria are easily cultivated in the laboratory and serve as hosts for the bacterial viruses or "phages." These are thus the most readily manipulated of the viruses, and studies of their behavior can be used to illuminate general virus problems such as host relations, genetic mutations, and strain differences.

BACTERIA.   It is not easy to give a neat and precise definition of bacteria. They are the smallest of organisms (if we take the usual course and do not call viruses "organisms"), the largest being barely visible under the light microscope. Ordinarily they appear to be single cells without a nucleus (though a nucleus can be demonstrated by special methods) and they seem to lack means of locomotion (though this again is more apparent than real). They are the things we commonly think of as "germs"; they are everywhere and perform a bewildering variety of functions in helping to maintain the normal operation of the biological community. Many of them are saprophytes, or agents of decay; many are involved in mutual symbiotic relations with other organisms; and many are parasitic, pathogenic. The human intestinal tract is the normal habitat of a considerable bacterial flora. When pathogenic forms take up residence there, they cause sore throat at one end, and diarrhea at the other. Pus-forming infections are bacterial, as are the causative agents of such diseases as diphtheria, tuberculosis, gonorrhea, common forms of pneumonia, cholera, and syphilis (though the spirochaetes of syphilis and their relatives are sometimes classed as protozoa). The various antibiotics have been particularly successful in the treatment of bacterial infections.

FUNGI. Some fungi are pathogenic for man, and cause a variety of skin infections, such as "athlete's foot"; they also sometimes are responsible for serious lung infections. Fungi are very important pathogens for many kinds of organisms, especially insects and seed plants.

PROTOZOA. Many different groups of protozoa have evolved parasitic habits. The most important human pathogens are the *Plasmodia* (Sporozoa, the causative agents of malaria), the trypanosomes (which broadly include a number of Hemo-flagellate genera that cause Leishmaniases, African sleeping-sickness, Chagas disease, and the like), and the pathogenic amebae.

HELMINTHS. The different kinds of parasitic worms are, for convenience, grouped together as "helminths" by the parasitologists, and they form the subject of a special science, helminthology. Human parasites include, in the phylum Platyhelminths, flukes of the class Trematoda (the cause of the disease schistosomiasis) and various tapeworms of the class Cestoda. A number of different nematodes are parasitic in man: hookworms, pinworms, trichina, ascaris, various kinds of filaria, and a few bizarre things such as the Guinea worm of the Old World tropics (Fig. 8-2).

OTHERS. The list of arthropods using man as a host is considerable—ticks, mites, bugs, fleas, mosquitoes, blackflies, and so on. Whether to

Fig. 8-2. Examples of parasitic "worms." (A) Tapeworm (Taenia solium), belonging to the class Cestoda of the phylum Platyhelminths; (B) roundworms (microfilaria); and (C) larval trichina (Trichinella spiralis) encysted in muscle.

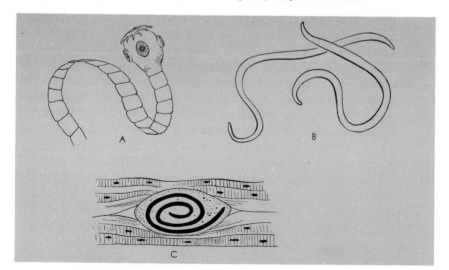

call an animal such as a mosquito (or a leech) "parasitic" is, of course, a matter of definition. Some insects, however, are parasitic by any definition; two examples are: the human botfly *(Dermatobia)* of tropical America, whose larvae grow in a boil-like sore in the skin, and the chigger-flea *(Tunga)* of many parts of the tropics, which finds the area under human toenails a fine place to produce a large batch of eggs.

THE ECOLOGY OF DISEASE

The study of the incidence and transmission of disease is the province of the special science of epidemiology, although this study could equally well be called the ecology or the natural history of disease. Epidemiology stems from *epidemic,* an unusual or severe outbreak of a disease. Epidemics have played an important role all through human history, and many minds have been devoted to analyzing and fighting them. The epidemic, the unusual situation, however, cannot be understood without a study of the endemic, or the more usual condition, in which the disease is scarcely noticed because it is a steady and continuing part of the community environment.

The word epidemiology can be applied very broadly, to cover such subjects as the causes and incidence of mental disorders, of accidents, or indeed of any sort of disease situation, but in the context of this book, we are concerned chiefly with the epidemiology of infectious disease, since this is basically a biological problem that is dependent on the interactions of hosts, pathogens, and environment. Incidence means numbers of cases, and epidemiology is in large part a statistical science, although the statistics are meaningless except in terms of the biology of the situation.

We are only beginning to understand the complicated host-parasite interactions in infectious disease. Some parasites are highly host-specific, that is, they attack only one species of animal, or perhaps only a single kind of tissue within the animal. Parasites which require two or more different hosts to complete their life cycle may be highly specific for both of the alternating hosts, though one might be an insect and one a mammal. Other parasites are less specific in their host relations. In general, related animals are apt to have related parasites, and particular parasites often seem to have a long evolutionary history of association with their hosts. But there are many exceptions; the only way we have of predicting the specificity of a parasite is to test it in the laboratory on numerous possible hosts. Many human pathogens are highly host-specific for man. This is true, for instance, of the viruses associated with the common cold, and it has greatly handicapped their study, since they cannot be tested on experimental animals.

Pathogens vary greatly in virulence, in the extent of damage they cause to the host. The same strain of pathogen may be highly virulent in one host and not in another. A given strain of yellow fever, for instance, may infect and multiply in a species of opossum with no apparent injury to the opossum, and at the same time be highly fatal for certain monkey species. Indeed, it may be fatal for one kind of monkey and harmless for another kind. Individuals of a given host species also may vary greatly in their reaction to a particular strain of pathogen, ranging from relatively resistant to susceptible. Differences in virulence of human pathogens at different times, or in different populations, are a commonplace in the history of disease, and many cases are described in the study by Zinsser cited in the Selected Readings at the end of the book.

There is always some sort of a serological (biochemical) reaction on the part of a host in which a parasite has become successfully established. These reactions are investigated by the sciences of serology and immunology. In many cases the parasite acts as an *antigen* which provokes the development of neutralizing *antibodies*. This is particularly clear with the viruses, and the course of the disease can be visualized as a race between virus multiplication and antibody production. With a pathogen such as the yellow fever virus, the host may be killed before the virus is controlled by antibody production, or the antibodies may win and the virus be eliminated. Some pathogens, especially many viruses like those causing yellow fever, smallpox, and measles, produce in the host, after one infection, the ability to continue manufacturing antibodies as long as it lives, and it thus remains *immune* to a second invasion of the same virus. We do not really understand this process: One theory holds that traces of the virus remain established in some part of the body and continue to stimulate antibody production. The principle of vaccination, with smallpox and yellow fever, is to infect the host with an innocuous strain of virus, making it immune to subsequent infection with virulent strains. With other viruses, like those of influenza, antibody production may be only temporary, so that the host presently is again susceptible to infection.

The self-limiting infections—smallpox and measles, for instance—must obviously have a continuing fresh supply of new hosts if they are to continue; such pathogens, then, are normally endemic in dense host populations and they reach scattered populations only as occasional epidemics.

A great many pathogens show an alternation of hosts, and are not normally directly contagious from one individual to another of a given host species. Four human diseases—schistosomiasis, malaria, yellow fever, and plague—will serve as examples of different kinds of transmission mechanisms.

SCHISTOSOMIASIS. Three species of blood flukes of the genus *Schistosoma* are pathogenic for man and are important agents of disease in some parts of the world. The life histories vary in detail, but the cycle generally starts with the eggs being passed out in human excreta; the miracidial larvae that hatch from the eggs must find certain species of aquatic snails to serve as intermediate hosts. After a period of development in the snail, worms called *cercariae* escape from the snails into the water in large numbers. If they encounter a mammal host in the two or three days that they are able to live, they bore into the skin (infection may also occur from drinking), develop into the adult phase, and start producing eggs again. The schistosomes that infect man may also infect other mammals with habits that bring them into snail-infested water.

MALARIA. Four species of the protozoan genus *Plasmodium* cause various forms of malaria in man. In the human host, the parasites live within the red blood cells; the parasites normally multiply asexually, but from time to time sexual forms, *gametocytes,* are developed. If these are picked up from the blood by an appropriate mosquito (of the genus *Anopheles*), the male forms *(microgametes)* burst from the host blood cell in the mosquito stomach and fuse there with the female *macrogametes.* The zygote which results penetrates the stomach wall, where it forms a cyst of multiplying cells that eventually burst out (in the form of *sporozoites*) and make their way through the mosquito body to the salivary glands. When the mosquito next bites, they are injected into a new vertebrate host. In the case of human malaria, the sporozoites first infect the liver so that there is an "exoerythrocytic" stage before the red blood cells become involved.

The human *Plasmodia* are all host-specific for man; other species attack primates besides man, as well as birds, lizards, and a few other vertebrates. All, as far as is known, have mosquito intermediate hosts, but different *Plasmodia* infect different kinds of mosquitoes.

YELLOW FEVER. There are two epidemiological patterns of yellow fever, one urban and one sylvatic. The pathogen is a virus which causes a self-limited infection in man (the human host either dies within around 12 days after infection or recovers with a lifetime immunity to re-infecton). In the urban form, the intermediate host is a mosquito, *Aedes aegypti,* which in tropical America, at least, is always closely associated with man, breeding in rain barrels, tin cans, vases, and so forth. When the mosquito bites a host with virus circulating in the blood stream, it becomes infective for new hosts after a period of about 12 days (the incubation period depends on the temperature) and remains infective for life (which, in the case of a mosquito, is usually short, at most 30 days or so). The virus was long thought to be host-specific for man, and since there is no other known host in urban areas, the virus requires a large human population for survival.

Under these circumstances, it seemed possible to eliminate yellow fever from the Western hemisphere by eliminating it from the large cities (like Rio de Janeiro) that served as foci of infection. When a campaign with this purpose was started, however, it was discovered that the disease also exists in remote parts of the upper Amazon and Orinoco river systems. where the *Aedes* mosquito does not live, and where the human population is small and scattered. It turned out that in these inland regions various species of monkeys served as the mammal host of the virus, and that

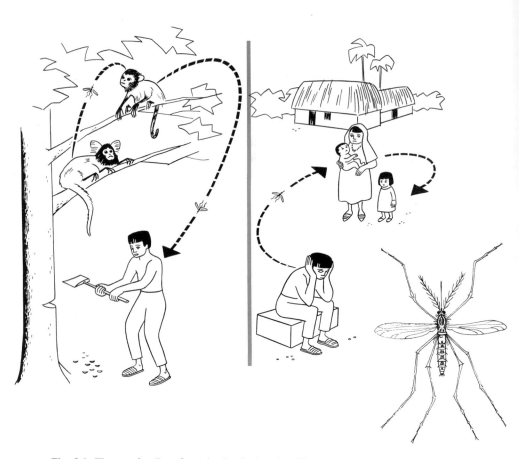

Fig. 8-3. Theory of yellow fever in South America. The virus is maintained in the forest in monkeys and forest mosquitoes, and man is only incidentally infected; however, an infected man, returning to a town, may start an urban epidemic, with the virus transmitted from man to man by the domestic Aedes mosquito (shown at right).

forest mosquitoes *(Haemagogus)* are the intermediate hosts; man enters the cycle only accidentally, though a man, infected in the forest, could return to a town or city and set off an urban epidemic (Fig. 8-3).

PLAGUE.   The Black Death, which caused such devastating epidemics in Europe in the Middle Ages, is still an important disease in some parts of the world, especially in India. It is now endemic in the western United States in wild rodents and causes occasional human deaths, providing a constant worry for public health officials. The pathogen is a bacterium, *Pasteurella pestis.* Plague shows several epidemiological patterns. Normally it is a disease of rodents, and the great epidemics of history involved both rat and human populations. The bacillus is ordinarily transmitted from rat to rat by fleas, and fleas may also carry it from rat to man and from man to man. In a severe human epidemic, a "pneumonic" form of the disease develops, which is directly contagious from man to man.

In the course of a plague outbreak in San Francisco in 1900, ground squirrels outside the city became infected, and a sylvatic form of the disease has persisted in the western United States despite all efforts to exterminate it. Some 18 species of wild rodents have been found to serve as hosts, and at least 30 species of fleas associated with these rodents are able to transmit the disease under laboratory conditions.

THE GEOGRAPHY OF DISEASE

With the development of modern transportation, most of the human contagions have become cosmopolitan, occurring wherever populations are dense enough to support them. The history of particular diseases is often obscure, because it is not always easy to interpret old records, but most of the contagions have probably existed in the centers of Old World population, around the Mediterranean and in the Orient, for a long time. Smallpox, we know, was brought to America among the followers of Cortez, and it can be plausibly argued that the disease, rather than the Spaniards, conquered Mexico. Smallpox, measles, and other diseases caused disastrous epidemics among both the American Indians and the people of the Pacific when they first came in contact with Europeans.

The diseases that rely on indirect methods of transmission do not move so easily, since suitable intermediate hosts must be present. In the case of malaria, species of *Anopheles* that can act as vectors of *Plasmodium* live in most warm regions of the world, and the disease has spread widely. African sleeping-sickness, on the other hand, has not become established outside the range of the tsetse fly vectors, *Glossina*. It is generally thought that yellow fever is a disease indigenous to Africa and that it spread to America with the slave trade. The urban vector, *Aedes aegypti,* also appears to have been originally an African species that has spread to all parts of the tropical world because of its ability to breed in the water containers of sailing vessels. Yellow fever, if this is correct, was able to establish itself secondarily in New World forest monkeys and mosquitoes. Plague, probably originally an Oriental disease, has similarly been able to become endemic among wild rodents in the New World.

MEDICINE AND PUBLIC HEALTH

Infectious disease is thus a biological phenomenon, and a great many biological principles can be illustrated by disease study. Other classes of diseases—deficiency, degenerative, and hereditary diseases—are also most readily understood in biological terms. But the emphasis in the study of these is physiological, while the infections involve both physiological and ecological considerations.

When we move our attention to the long catalogue of mental illnesses, we are on less certain biological grounds. Hereditary—genetic—factors are often at their root, and although physiological malfunctioning frequently accompanies mental disorders, biological explanations of psychoses and neuroses have generally proven to be inadequate. These diseases result from defects in the human personality, and they so far have eluded dissection with the biologist's scalpel. Our progress in understanding and controlling mental disease is retarded indeed when compared with our achievements with infections. The problem clearly involves both biological and social sciences, and we have yet to find effective ways of blending these approaches.

Medicine, then, is not simply "applied biology." It is this and a great deal besides. If we shift our gaze from curative medicine to preventive medicine, to public health, the scope broadens even more. Public health is truly human ecology, since the welfare of the community depends on the countless interactions among people and between people and the environment. Public health started with sanitary engineering, with problems of sewage disposal and water supply, but the need to apply the knowledge of many other fields became more and more pressing, and the effectiveness of public health programs, in the present century, has consequently increased enormously. Engineering, medical, biological, and social sciences all contribute to the work of modern public health organizations, so that the boundaries between the particular sciences become more and more meaningless.

The health of the human community clearly involves much more than freedom from disease. One could argue that the most important aspects of a community's health are far outside the field of biology, or even of any of the subjects ordinarily thought of as part of "public health." The values and satisfactions, the morals, of both individuals and groups, are surely basic to the development of a healthy society, and these things can hardly be dealt with by biology, perhaps not by any science.

But this is far from saying that biology is irrelevant except in connection with medicine and agriculture. We are slowly coming to realize that the health of the human community depends in many ways on the health of the biological community as a whole, that the health of man is linked with the health of the forests, seas, streams, and soils. These relationships between the human community and the planetary environment are often studied as *conservation*. In some ways this is an unfortunate label. Conserving is important, to be sure, but it carries connotations of static and miserly hoarding against the future. The problem is larger than that of conservation, preservation, or protection. It is a problem of using as well as of preserving; a problem of living with nature as well as of protecting nature; a problem, in the largest sense, of keeping the system of the human community in balance with the system of nature, because if the two get too far out of accord, man's proud society will end by destroying itself. We can perhaps most appropriately look at this in terms of the relations between the two sciences of ecology and economics.

Ecology
and Economics

CHAPTER NINE

If we look at the words *ecology* and *economics* (or *economy*), their derivation appears to be very similar. The *eco-* (from *oikos*) means "house" or "household" in both cases. *Logos* is "word" or, perhaps better, "discourse." *Nemein* is "to manage." We have, then, "discourse on the household" versus "management of the household." Although talking and acting are two very different things, our formulation of the issue hardly helps us to understand the distinction between ecology and economics as the two words are used today. They have come to apply to subject matters that are apparently quite different—but the difference may be more apparent than real.

The "household" of ecology is that of the living world, the biosphere; of economics, that of the human species alone. Ecology is concerned with food-webs, temperature tolerances, nitrogen cycles, dispersal mechanisms; economics with labor, markets, bank discount rates, per capita income. The vocabularies certainly look very different, yet, fundamentally, both are concerned with the same "household," that of our planet Earth. The separation is an accident of the history of scholarship, rather than a reflection of any profound cleavage of subject matter. Let us start by looking at ecology in terms of the economy of nature.

THE ECONOMY OF NATURE

The biological community ordinarily is a self-maintaining system, dependent on the sun as an external source of energy, but otherwise self-sufficient. If we examine the history of carbon, oxygen, nitrogen, water, or any other constituent of living processes, we find that it involves a series of cycles in which materials are passed from organism to organism and between organisms and the inorganic environment. Nothing is lost and almost nothing is transformed into a state that removes it from the cycle. We have to say "almost nothing" because a tiny proportion of the organic materials does accumulate as geological sediments (like coal and oil) that are then outside the cycling process.

We are becoming increasingly aware of the extent to which the organic and inorganic environments on the surface of our planet are interrelated. We all realize that oxygen and carbon dioxide, as atmospheric gases, are necessary for life as we know it; but it also appears that their presence in the atmosphere is a consequence of life. We now believe that the original atmosphere of the earth was very different from the present one, perhaps composed of gases such as methane and ammonia. The living material that formed in this environment would be different from anything that has survived, and with the beginning of the process of organic evolution, the alteration of the chemical environment also started. This had probably reached about its present state by the time our fossil record begins, perhaps half way between the first living stuff and the present. It has been calculated that the carbon dioxide in the atmosphere is now cycled through the living system every 300 years, and the oxygen every 2,000 years.

The chemical composition of sea water, like that of the atmosphere, is both a consequence of the living process, and a necessary condition for it. At one time it was thought that the salts of the sea were constantly increasing through additions from erosion of the land, and that the age of the seas could be determined by calculating how long it would take for the present salt content to accumulate. But by this calculation the seas turn out to be only a few tens of millions of years old, while all other evidence indicates that they have an age of many hundreds of millions of years. Further, it seems likely that the seas have had about the same chemical composition since the beginning of the Cambrian, despite annual additions from the land. How else explain the close similarity in proportions of chemical ions between all kinds of protoplasm and sea water itself? Land and fresh-water organisms are packets of sea water that have found ways of maintaining themselves in a different environment—but they still carry the mark of the ancient seas in which they started.

We have not worked out all of the chemical cycles of the sea with any precision. With calcium, we can see the process easily enough: It is constantly being removed from the sea by corals, molluscs, and a variety of other organisms and accumulated as limestone, which over the eons is gradually dissolved again. Sodium is removed much more slowly, perhaps mostly through inorganic processes that have led to the formation of the great salt deposits in many parts of the world. It is also added very slowly —the sodium chloride content of most river water is very low. Each of the chemicals of the sea thus has its own cycle.

Soil, obviously enough, is one of the factors governing the kind of vegetation that will grow in a particular place, but the characteristics of a particular soil are also the consequence of the kind of vegetation that has been growing on it. The various soil types result from the mineral composition of the soil-producing rocks and from the character of the climate—and from the actions of living organisms, worms as well as trees and grass.

The biosphere, the zone of life over the surface of the planet, is thus a dynamic system in which living and inorganic processes are interlocked. The processes, as far as we can tell, have been essentially the same through the whole period of the paleontological record. At the start of this record, our present categories of producers, consumers, and decomposers are all recognizable, although, to be sure, only in the marine environment. We can observe the extension of the system to fresh water and to land, and see the evolution of some complex subsystems such as those of flowering plants and insects. But beyond this the changes have largely been matters of detail.

The total mass of living stuff, the "biomass," on the planet has been about the same for a long time, probably at least from the beginning of the Cenozoic, and perhaps since the Mesozoic. Species, genera, and families have come and gone, in what G. G. Simpson has aptly called a "relay effect." One species has passed on its role in the economy of nature to another species; the system marches on, but the kinds of processes have not changed.

With the advent of man as a maker of tools and as a producer of food, new relationships were introduced into the system. The biosphere started to transform into the noösphere, started to become dominated by the phenomenon of the human mind. In another way, we could say that the biosphere started changing from a system-in-itself into a "resource" for one of its component species, *Homo sapiens*. This raises many problems— for the biosphere and for *Homo sapiens*.

RESOURCES: RENEWABLE AND NONRENEWABLE

The word "resource" immediately implies a point of view; things are resources only in relation to some purpose. Resources for squirrels and robins, presumably, would be the materials *they* needed for food, shelter, dispersal, and so on. But we do not ordinarily use the word in this way. Resources are what *we* need to survive and prosper.

For man, resources mean many things. The resources of the North American continent were quite different for pre-Columbian Indians and for the invading Europeans. The resources of the continent for the Europeans were different in the eighteenth century and in the twentieth. Uranium, to cite an obvious example, has become a resource within our own lifetime. The meaning of resources for man, in other words, depends on human culture much more than on human biology. When we start thinking about resources, we move from ecology to economics. Man, however, still forms part of the biosphere, resources remain a part of the environment, and the points of view of ecology and economics should be blended in dealing with them.

The resources of civilized man are usually classified as either *renewable* or *nonrenewable*. Renewable resources are those that have the inherent capacity to replace and maintain themselves if managed wisely. Examples are plants and animals, either wild or domesticated, that can ordinarily maintain their numbers from generation to generation, despite losses to man, by utilizing more of their reproductive potentials. Water, too, is a renewable resource when it is drawn from the normal hydrologic cycle; but in some places man is currently tapping "fossil water," water that has accumulated in underground reservoirs from past geologic times, and this, when it is exhausted, cannot be renewed.

Nonrenewable resources are those that, in practical or foreseeable terms, cannot be replaced—that have no inherent capacity to maintain themselves. No materials are actually lost from the planet, but man changes many things from forms that he can use into forms that he cannot. Iron that has rusted and disintegrated into the soil cannot be recovered even though the iron atoms are all still there. Materials involved in cycles too long for human management are also nonrenewable. The petroleum and coal used by man every year represent the accumulations of millions of years, and they are lost beyond recovery as they are burned. Soil is a resource that can be maintained through wise management, but its fertility can be so destroyed in a few years by mismanagement that it will need a thousand years to be restored. For our purposes, then, it becomes nonrenewable.

The resources that supported primitive man were mostly renewable. We might argue that man began to dip into the reserves of nature when he started chipping flints, but he did not tap nonrenewable resources in any significant way until he learned to use metals. Deposits of gold, silver, copper, iron, and so forth, cannot be replenished after they are mined. Surface deposits were soon depleted, and man had to embark on ever more complex operations of mining and exploration in distant areas.

Man's first energy sources, wood and charcoal, were in theory renewable, although he often cleared forests with such abandon that they became, in effect, nonrenewable, as can be observed by any visitor to the Mediterranean. During the Industrial Revolution, man began burning up vast quantities of irreplaceable fossil fuels—coal, then oil and gas.

So far man has been doing all right. He has discovered new reserves of metals and of fuels faster than he can consume them, but this, as the pessimists point out, cannot go on indefinitely. Man has been using nonrenewable resources on a large scale for only a couple of hundred years, which is trivial in terms of human history and hardly a moment in geological time. No one pretends that oil or coal or even easily mined iron will last forever. The optimists, on the other hand, disregard the dwindling reserves and place their confidence in man's ingenuity. As we exhaust one material, they assume we will find or invent others. Steel will be replaced by plastics that can be made from renewable materials, oil by alcohol that can be distilled from crops. And if man can learn to tap solar energy directly, he need worry no more about an energy supply.

The optimists and the pessimists both make good cases: Man has proved himself to be ingenious, but he has also proved himself to be wasteful and destructive. The problem is a large one, and should be of concern to every thoughtful citizen. It involves questions of technology, economics, and social organization that are far outside the province of biology, but it is also biological insofar as it is concerned with man's relations with other living things. Maintaining our renewable resources clearly calls for wise management (Fig. 9-1). We need intelligent handling of soils, streams, forests, and wildlife. Since all these activities depend in large part on our knowledge of biology, let us look at the biological aspects of some of these problems.

WILDLIFE MANAGEMENT

It has been estimated that hunters and fishermen in the United States spend about ten billion dollars a year on their hobby—an estimate based on the calculation that 25 million sportsmen average 400 dollars each. Whatever the exact figures, there is no doubt that this is big business, which becomes even bigger if commercial fisheries and fur-trapping are added. It can only continue if adequate populations of fish, birds, and mammals are maintained, and this job has become the principal aim of the fisheries and wildlife experts. Wildlife management is now a considerable profession in the United States, with its own special college departments, technical journals, and professional societies. It is essentially applied ecology—although, as always, the line between "applied" and "pure" is not clear-cut, and some of the most basic ecological studies have been made under wildlife auspices.

We have created a complex system of national, state, and local game laws designed to secure an adequate game supply in the face of a changing landscape and increasing numbers of hunters. Many of the laws were passed before our ecological knowledge of the problem was very adequate, and the fact that almost every hunter considers himself a wildlife expert only

Fig. 9-1. "Going the Indian
one better." (Courtesy of
the Jay N. "Ding" Darling
Foundation.)

compounds the difficulty. But we are coming to realize the need for scientific study and management if we are to preserve the pioneer tradition of hunting and woodcraft in our urbanized and industrialized society.

Our concern is relatively new. California set aside the first game refuge in the United States in 1870. Yellowstone National Park was established in 1872—the first national park in the world. The idea behind Yellowstone was not so much conservation as the preservation of natural wonders, and wildlife in the park was not given full protection until 1894. After the turn of the century, the conservation movement gained considerable impetus from the interest and enthusiasm of Theodore Roosevelt and his friend Gifford Pinchot, who was America's first professional forester, and a good enough politician to become governor of Pennsylvania. Many of our political leaders since then have recognized the importance of husbanding our natural resources, including wildlife, and the areas of national parks, national forests, and game refuges of various sorts have been extended. Efforts to create a unified Department of Conservation within the federal government, however, have so far failed.

One objective of wildlife management is to prevent the extinction of rare species of birds and mammals. Something over a hundred kinds of mammals and a similar number of birds have become extinct since the time of Christ, all as a consequence of man's activities, and there is a long list of many hundreds of species currently in danger.*

In the present century, an average of one mammal species and one bird species has become extinct somewhere in the world every year, and the rate is likely to increase with the rapid expansion of human population and the exploitation of the remaining wild regions of the world.

What difference does it make, one may ask, whether the passenger pigeon (Fig. 9-2) and the dodo have disappeared, and the whooping crane may go tomorrow? It may be difficult to make a case for each individual species, but the total process becomes frightening. Is there no room on the planet except for man and the few other animals that can get along in his gardens, orchards, and city parks? Have we the right to destroy the rest of nature? Does our might make right? And beyond this lurks the

* Glover M. Allen, *Extinct and Vanishing Mammals of the Western Hemisphere;* Francis Harper, *Extinct and Vanishing Mammals of the Old World;* and James G. Greenway, Jr., *Extinct and Vanishing Birds of the World,* all published in New York by the American Committee for International Wild Life Protection.

Fig. 9-2. Photograph of the last living passenger pigeon, 1911. (Courtesy National Aubudon Society.)

Fig. 9-3. The marten is among the animals requiring large wilderness areas for survival. (Courtesy American Museum of Natural History.)

uncomfortable question of whether, in wantonly destroying the rest of nature, we may not end by destroying ourselves.

These are large questions, without ready answers. In most cases, extinction is caused not so much by direct human action in killing animals, as by the indirect effects of man's alteration of the habitat. Untold millions of passenger pigeons were, indeed, slaughtered, but many ecologists believe they were doomed anyway by the destruction of the great forest that once covered the eastern United States. Their breeding habits and food habits were not adapted to the changing landscape. The bison of the Great Plains, attacked with equal destructiveness, were saved by last-minute action, and the habits of the bison have fortunately enabled the species to survive on a reservation.

Many animals—the caribou, marten (Fig. 9-3), and wolverine, for example —require large wilderness areas for survival, and populations of these animals continue to decline, despite protection, as the wilderness decreases.

But perhaps man, too, needs wilderness, some place where he can occasionally escape from his own turmoil, noise, and litter. The interests of farmers, hunters, nature lovers, engineers, lumbermen, and ranchers frequently clash over these conservation questions, and there is not enough concern for the common interest, the common good. This is not an easy responsibility to assume, but it is an urgent one.

FORESTRY

Forests form the natural cover of the land wherever conditions of rainfall and temperature permit, wherever it is neither too cold nor too dry. There are many kinds of forests, from the coniferous forests of the far north to the rain forests of the mid-tropics, and the type depends on local conditions of climate and soil. Thousands of species of plants belonging to a wide variety of different families have assumed the tree form. The bamboos are really tree grasses, and in the tropics some of the compositae, plants of the daisy family, are trees. In the geological past, mosses and ferns were giants.

Forest formation, in short, seems to be the general tendency of vegetation on land under favorable conditions, perhaps because it allows the vegetation to take maximum advantage of sunlight by filtering it down through many layers of foliage.

The forest is not composed of trees alone. They form the basic structure and may include the largest bulk of protoplasm, but they serve also as support for woody vines (lianas) and for epiphytes (plants which perch on their branches and trunks). In the tropical rain forest, lianas may account for as much as a third of the foliage of the canopy, and there is a fantastic variety of epiphytes rooted on the trees, of which orchids are the most familiar to us. On the forest floor live the plants that can grow in the deep shade, the sort of plants we grow in the dim light of hotel lobbies. And living off this mass of vegetation—and off each other—are the animals in their endless variety. The forests become less complex as we move from the ample rainfall and continuous warmth of the mid-tropics to regions of seasonal cold or drought. But the great deciduous forest that covered the eastern United States in colonial times must still have been an impressive formation, judging from the accounts of the early explorers, and we can imagine that the forests of Stone Age Europe were similar. Of these forests we now have only rare and tattered remnants.

Man learned to clear forests long ago, since the forest can be defeated with stone axes more easily than grasslands can be plowed with wooden sticks. The first agriculture probably took place in openings where trees were cut or girdled and burned, and as man became more civilized, more adept at destroying the forest, he replaced it with field crops, pastures, and the scattered, small trees of orchards. This vegetation proved of great value, but we have not yet learned how to use the forest formation efficiently, even though it is the most effective natural system for absorbing the energy of the sun to build up organic materials. As man exhausts the stored capital of coal, oil, and iron, he may have to learn to rely more on the renewable resources of the forests, which could turn out to be enormous, especially if and when we learn to utilize cellulose and lignin as basic raw materials for foods and chemicals.*

Forests, of course, have long been sources for timber and fuel, and the unfortunate effects of forest destruction were recognized in classical Greece and Rome. William Penn, in 1681, decreed that one acre of forest must be left in Pennsylvania for every five acres cleared, but there was no way of enforcing the decree. The need for scientific management of forests was recognized in western Europe early in the nineteenth century, and in the United States the American Forestry Association was formed in 1875. A forest agency was organized in the Department of Agriculture a year later, but it was not until 1891, under President Harrison, that the first

* The possibilities for forest products are pointed out by Egon Glesinger in *The Coming Age of Wood* (New York: Simon & Schuster, 1949).

national forest reserves were established. Although these have been expanded greatly in the succeeding years, we still have failed to set a national policy that will guarantee a balance between cutting and growth.

Forests not only provide lumber and pulpwood; they are also crucial in the regulation of erosion, floods, and soil. The Tennessee Valley Authority has demonstrated convincingly how dam building and reforestation can be combined with river control, but we have not carried this concept very far in planning for other regions of the world. Nor have we been very wise in the management of our streams—which brings us to the problem of pollution.

POLLUTION

Every organism produces wastes, and gets rid of them through excretion. These waste materials do not pollute the biological community, however, because they fit into the unending cycles of materials and energy within the community. The waste of one organism becomes the food of another, and the whole class of organisms called decomposers (mostly bacteria and fungi) is busily engaged in cleaning up the debris that would otherwise accumulate. Here again man, especially industrial man, has introduced new

Fig. 9-4. Los Angeles on one of its frequent smoggy days. (Wide World Photos.)

factors into the system of nature which cannot be compensated for by the slow process of evolution. Man has made the mess, dumped the filth and poisons into his environment; unless he learns to clean it up, he will have to live with it, with unknown consequences for his health and that of his descendants.

Much of the pollution problem results from the simple arithmetic of human numbers. The excretory products of any animal are ordinarily handled easily enough by the natural decomposing system, but men, multiplying and concentrating in cities, have developed volumes of sewage that overwhelm the ordinary decomposition process. The excrement of a large city, when drained into a stream, lake, or harbor, often destroys the self-cleansing abilities of the water and kills the native biota—and raises a stench to boot. The problem is so obvious that much has been done to counteract it, and sewage disposal can now be accomplished without pollution.

Other pollution problems, less easily solved, stem from industrial activities. Smog smothers the air around our cities (Fig. 9-4). Oil wastes destroy waterfowl, fish, and vegetation—and annoy swimmers. The chemical by-products of industry poison our streams and turn the nearby countryside into dreary wastelands. Awareness of the dangers of this kind of pollution has been late in coming, and we still have not found ways to control it.

These problems, serious though they are, fade before those created by man's discovery of nuclear fission. The extent of the damage from increased radiation spewn out by atomic explosions is a subject of bitter argument among the experts, but no one denies that the long-term consequences could be serious. Even if all nations agree not to drop any more bombs, we must somehow dispose of the radioactive wastes produced by the peaceful use of atomic energy. The bright picture of the future based on man's control of the atom is still marred by the question: What do we do with the waste products? The answer, at least partly, rests in the hands of biologists.

Man's fantastic accomplishment in learning to utilize nuclear fission still has not freed him from the system of nature. He has multiplied his power, and also multiplied his need for wisdom—but he seems to acquire wisdom more slowly than power.

Science, Man, and Nature

CHAPTER TEN

Francis Bacon expressed the paradox of man and nature neatly with the aphorism, "We cannot command nature except by obeying her." Mankind is a part of nature, subject to the force of gravitation, to the laws of energy transfer, to the need for food and reproduction. Yet, at the same time, mankind is apart from nature in the possession of the curious quality of awareness, of the ability to analyze and describe, to think, and to record and communicate thoughts. As men, we can be detached and contemplative, at least to a certain degree. We can look at nature, study it, and change it in many ways. Mankind can be viewed as a new sort of geological force, reshaping the landscape, favoring some kinds of organisms and destroying others, changing the very composition of the atmosphere with the smoke of countless chimneys, starting new chains of radioactive decay with atomic explosions.

In this book we have sketched something of the history of man's changing relations with nature. The protohominids and Paleolithic men over some hundreds of thousands of years could be considered as integral parts of the biological communities in which they lived, fitting into the patterns of food cycles as predators, gatherers, hosts, and prey. There was a drastic change in these relations about 12,000 years ago with the Neolithic Revolution, with the shift from food-collecting to food-producing and with the development of agriculture; man started the process of changing the community by clearing away vegetation he did not want, and replacing it with crops he could use.

Further changes in man's relations with biological communities were produced about 5,000 years ago by the Urban Revolution, the beginning of cities and civilization. The key change here, the discovery of methods of storing and transporting food and other materials, led to the development of trade routes and the exchange of goods so that men became more and more independent of the resources of any one particular biological community. Cities, city-states, and empires appeared. The new techniques resulted in a great increase in human numbers.

Then the Industrial Revolution, which started two hundred years or so ago, enabled man to control new and vast sources of power—steam, electricity, and now the atom—and put him into an even more special position in the system of nature.

THE SCIENTIFIC REVOLUTION

The growth of modern science parallels rather closely the development of the Industrial Revolution. The two phenomena have been closely related, yet they have also been in many ways independent. The men who invented machinery, designed factory production methods, and built industrial empires were rarely interested in the abstract ideas of science. And the key figures in the history of science, men like Galileo (1564–1642), Newton (1642–1727), Faraday (1791–1867), and Darwin (1809–1882), were rarely concerned with the practical applications of their ideas. Industry and science did not really form a close alliance in England and the United States until after 1900, though close relations were developed earlier in Germany. The consequences of this alliance in our own times have been spectacular—the electric and electronic industries are examples—and the possibilities for the future sometimes seem almost limitless. As C. P. Snow * has suggested, we might well call the development of this relation between science and industry the Scientific Revolution, and regard it as distinct from the preceding Industrial Revolution.

We now have, at least in the countries with "advanced" economies, an abundance of goods and services for everyone which even the privileged few could not command a century ago. We have a wide variety of machines to replace physical labor, giving leisure time to all ranks of society. We have achieved a remarkable degree of control over disease and physical

* C. P. Snow, *The Two Cultures and the Scientific Revolution* (New York: Cambridge University Press, 1959). The problems of the relations between scientists and humanists, discussed later in this chapter, are also developd in this little book.

pain. We are, it seems, at the dawn of the "space age," and the fantasies of yesterday's science fiction become the realities of tomorrow.

Yet our time has also been called the "age of anxiety." We have goods and services, but we don't quite know what to do with them. We have leisure, but we are not sure how to use it for the greatest satisfactions. We can control physical disease, but we calm our nerves with great quantities of tranquilizers and alcohol; we can scarcely provide room enough in our hospitals for the mentally ill. Utopia is here—and we are afraid.

If it is true that we have gained power faster than we have gained wisdom, without wisdom we may have gained power only to destroy ourselves. There are, certainly, many frightening aspects to the modern world. There is the ever-present threat of catastrophic, utterly destructive war. But beyond this there is the dizzy rate of increase of human populations, which greatly handicaps economic development in many parts of the world. Somewhat more remotely, there is the danger of the exhaustion of non-renewable resources and the impairment of resources like soils and forests that ought to be renewable.

The problem of our age, then, is to gain the wisdom we need to use our growing power intelligently. The many people who have been, and still are, searching for a solution to this problem have come to realize that there is no single solution, no single road to wisdom, understanding, and contentment. The whole process of education is a search for solutions, and this explains why modern educators insist on a diversity of educational experience. We can clearly learn much from the past experience of mankind, and gain from it a broad perspective we would otherwise lack in facing the future. The great figures of philosophical and religious thought have much to tell us. So do the artists—the poets, painters, and musicians—if we can learn to receive what they are trying to communicate to us. But what about science?

One can argue that science has played a basic part in forming both the material and the intellectual world in which modern man lives, and that consequently the study of science should be fundamental in modern education. On the other side, one can argue that science is the cause of our troubles and that it should be countered in education by greater stress on the arts and humanities. More sensibly, one can search for some middle way in which science is treated as one of the most powerful activities shaping human destiny, but in which it is not worshiped as the only road to truth and understanding.

THE TWO CULTURES: SCIENTIFIC AND HUMANISTIC

It is curious how often students dislike science courses. They take them only because they are required and try to meet the requirement with a minimum of effort. Science to them seems to be an irrelevant subject, full of strange, jawbreaking words to be memorized and forgotten as soon as the final examination has been passed, of frogs and worms to be cut up, of half-forgotten algebra and esoteric formulas. The great ideas of science never come across, nor does the excitement of discovery, or a feeling for the people, great and small, who have built up this immense body of knowledge. Almost all of us like the products of science—automobiles, modern medicine, television, wide varieties of food—but few of us have much curiosity about how these things came about.

The material benefits of science are clear, but the pervasive influence of science on how we think is little understood. We now know a great deal about the earth and the sun and the moon. How could we ever assume the old common sense attitude and view the earth as obviously flat with an arched firmament above it? We no longer appease the demons that hurl thunderbolts, or exorcise those that cause disease. We may worry about gremlins and black cats and the thirteenth floor, but it is a sort of play-worry, not the real terror of the unknown and unpredictable. We have almost imperceptibly acquired a faith in the orderliness of nature and, in some cases, at least, in its predictability. We may not know the second law of thermodynamics, but gravitation, evolution, and even relativity have become common words in our lexicon.

Intellectuals of many sorts tend to be scornful of science, and remain unconscious of the fact that the intellectual climate in which they live has been largely formed by science. Scientists themselves, as C. P. Snow has pointed out, often are not considered to be "intellectuals." The word is reserved for writers, artists, philosophers, and the like. Working scientists, on the other hand, are often scornful of other kinds of scholars, dismissing them as "fuzzy thinkers" chained by long outmoded traditions of knowledge. Snow, interviewing thousands of scientists in England during the Second World War, found them in general to be amazingly ignorant of literature and art—as he found writers and artists to be ignorant of science. The result is "two cultures" which have little contact with one another. It sometimes looks as though our intellectual world were as sharply split between scientists and humanists as the political world is between communists and advocates of democracy. Divided worlds, whether political or intellectual, are dangerous; and for the intellectual division there is little excuse.

Science is one of the great creative achievements of the human mind. The motivations, the satisfactions, the frustrations of the scientist are hardly different in kind from those of any other type of creative personality, however different the products of the creative act may be. The products in the case of science are concepts, theories, and classifications, arrived at by experiment, observation, and analysis. These certainly are very different from poems or paintings or symphonies, but they are no less great as intellectual accomplishments, no less worthy of our admiration and appreciation. Instead of contrasting sciences with humanities, perhaps we'd better look at the sciences as a part of the humanities, as one of the ways in which man has tried to understand himself and the world around him.

Our separation of science as a special and distinct kind of intellectual activity is relatively new—though nonetheless unfortunate. We can recognize many instances of scientific exploration in the ancient and medieval worlds, but the people involved generally called themselves philosophers, whatever the system they used in their inquiries. The founders of modern science in the seventeenth century still thought of themselves as philosophers and considered that they were dealing with the traditional problems of philosophy, even though they were approaching them untraditionally.

The student of science today is most often awarded the degree of "Doctor of Philosophy," but the label is about all that is left of the historic connection. There has been, in recent years, a considerable effort to develop a "philosophy of science" that would help bridge the gap, but this has not met with great encouragement from either scientists or philosophers. The trouble, one suspects, is that science *is* philosophy, today as well as yesterday—not all of philosophy, certainly, but a very live and active part that has somehow lost its family relationship, to the detriment of everyone.

Henry Margenau, physicist *and* philosopher at Yale, has well remarked: *

Much has been said about the conflict between the sciences and the humanities or the liberal arts. There is no root in history for this dichotomy, for science has its beginnings as a kind of philosophy. And if the term liberal is interpreted in the sense of liberating from prejudice, want, fear, and bondage to nature, then there is no art more liberating than science itself.

VALUES OF BIOLOGY

Biology has its share of creative personalities and great ideas, and they are fine examples of the high achievement of which mankind is capable. There is Linnaeus with his system of classification of animals and plants, which has served as a valid method of analyzing the living world for over 200 years. We have Darwin and his theory of evolution through natural selection; Pasteur and his theory of infection as a cause of disease; Mendel and his unit theory of heredity. How much credit each of these men should get for his insight is a matter for debate, which is true in the case of any man and his discovery. The ideas may be a consequence of the "ripeness of the times," but it still takes greatness to find and express them.

The practical and technological aspects of biology are largely found in the fields of medicine and agriculture. Indeed, these two fields long antedate, as do most technologies, what we ordinarily mean by the words

* In a conference on the history, philosophy, and sociology of science held by the American Philosophical Society and reported in the *Proceedings* of the Society, vol. 99 (1955), pp. 325–354.

Students interested in pursuing the matter of the nature of science will find the following books valuable: C. H. Waddington, *The Scientific Attitude,* rev. ed. (Pelican Books, 1948); Agnes Arber, *The Mind and the Eye: A Study of the Biologist's Standpoint* (New York: Cambridge University Press, 1954); and J. B. Conant, *On Understanding Science* (New Haven: Yale University Press, 1947; also published as a Mentor paperback).

"science" and "scientific theory." The changes in medicine and agriculture produced by the Scientific Revolution are profound, and even greater changes seem likely in the near future. Since the lives of us all depend on medicine and agriculture, it behooves us to know something about the science that is guiding them.

Biology, perhaps more than any of the other sciences, has a recreational value. There are many hobby possibilities. Natural-history collecting—of insects, plants, shells—has a long and honorable history, and many amateurs have made important contributions to science through such activities. But it isn't necessary to collect *things;* collections of observations can be equally rewarding and interesting, as the bird-watchers have demonstrated. It is easy to poke fun at bird-watching, but the watchers obviously find great satisfaction in it, and many have discovered habits and life histories that would otherwise go unnoticed by researchers. The fascinating world of shallow water has been opened for amateur exploration—with masks and snorkels, or with more elaborate equipment—and fish-watching may presently rival bird-watching in popularity. Gardening, hunting, photography—any outdoor experience—can be enhanced if it is based on some biological background.

But the greatest value of biology may well be what it can contribute to our general knowledge of nature, and of man's role in nature. We should know something about our bodies and how they work, something about the structure and workings of trees, birds, insects, and flowers. Morphology, physiology, genetics, embryology—a whole series of biological sciences illuminates these facets of nature. The ecological and behavioral aspects of biology also increase the degree of our understanding. The squirrel scolding in the oak tree, the robin on the lawn, and the trout in the stream can have significant meaning for us only when we know something about how they fit into the economy of nature. We can admire a landscape without knowing its biological structure, just as we can enjoy a symphony without a knowledge of harmony, or a painting without familiarity with the problems of perspective and design. But our appreciation, in all these cases, can be deepened through knowledge.

Curiously, as we become enmeshed in our cities and highway systems and in our busy everyday lives, and thus more removed from nature, we seem to yearn for a greater contact with a world not completely altered by our own activities. We are a part of nature still, and we cannot escape the uncomfortable question of how much of nature we can destroy without destroying ourselves. For our own satisfaction, our own salvation, we need to develop an "ecological conscience." And this perhaps is the ultimate value of biology, that it can restore to us a needed humility which, in the arrogance of our accomplishments, we have tended to lose. Even if we never manage to "understand" our world, we can at least learn to appreciate it—and to enjoy it, in a less selfish and less destructive way.

SELECTED READINGS

Anderson, Edgar, *Plants, Man and Life*. Boston: Little, Brown, 1952. Discusses many aspects of man's effect on the landscape, especially his relations with weeds and cultigens.

Brown, Harrison, *The Challenge of Man's Future*. New York: Viking, 1954. Perhaps the most balanced and inclusive of the various surveys of the problems of human populations and resources.

Coon, C. S., *The Story of Man*. New York: Knopf, 1954. An anthropologist surveys man's progress from the Stone Age to the present.

Dart, Raymond, with Dennis Craig, *Adventures with the Missing Link*. New York: Harper, 1959. Dart tells the story of the discovery of the Australopithecine fossils and of the attempts to reconstruct their way of life.

Dobzhansky, Theodosius, *Mankind Evolving*. New Haven: Yale University Press, 1962. A fine summary of our present knowledge of human evolution.

Eiseley, Loren, *Darwin's Century*. New York: Doubleday, 1958. The history of nineteenth-century evolutionary thought, including the development of opinion on man's place in the scheme of things.

Haskins, Caryl P., *Of Societies and Men*. New York: Norton, 1951. A biologist looks at human—and insect—societies.

Hooton, Earnest, *Man's Poor Relations*. New York: Doubleday, 1942. A survey of the primates, written in Hooton's usual lively style.

LaBarre, Weston, *The Human Animal*. Chicago: University of Chicago Press, 1954. LaBarre looks at human evolution and culture from the points of view of both anthropology and clinical psychology.

Thomas, W. L., Jr., ed., *Man's Role in Changing the Face of the Earth*. Chicago: University of Chicago Press, 1956. A mine of information about many aspects of man's relations with the natural world.

Zinsser, Hans, *Rats, Lice and History*. Boston: Little, Brown, 1935. A broad look at the history of diseases, and at the role of diseases in history.

Index